Reducing Stress

David Hazard

HARVEST HOUSE PUBLISHERS
Eugene, Oregon 97402

All Scripture quotations are taken from the King James Version of the Bible.

Cover by Left Coast Design, Portland, Oregon

Advisory

Readers are advised to consult with their physician or other medical practitioner before implementing the suggestions that follow.

This book is not intended to take the place of sound medical advice or to treat specific maladies. Neither the author nor the publisher assumes any liability for possible adverse consequences as a result of the information contained herein.

REDUCING STRESS
Copyright © 2002 by David Hazard
Published by Harvest House Publishers
Eugene, Oregon 97402

Library of Congress Cataloging-in-Publication Data
Hazard, David.
    Reducing stress   /   David Hazard.
       p. cm.
    ISBN 0-7369-0481-6
    1. Stress (Psychology)   2. Stress (Psychology)—Religious aspects.   3. Stress
management.   I. Title.
BF575.S75 H397 2001
155.9'042—dc21

                                                        2001016945

Printed in the United States of America.

02 03 04 05 06 07 / BP-BG / 10 9 8 7 6 5 4 3 2 1

Contents

*Special thanks to
Brian D.F. Richmond, M.P.H.,
for his review and advice in the
development of this book.*

Healthy Body, Healthy Soul

We human beings are marvels of creation. The sacred writings of most major religions testify to our amazing construction.

The ancient Hebrews, for instance, believed each of us was created with a sacred spark, made up of the passions that make us uniquely *us*. Around this inner fire were woven bone, sinew, muscle, and flesh, completing the whole person. With this vision of humankind—as amazingly integrated beings—they saw themselves as the "fearfully and wonderfully made" creatures we truly are![1]

A later, *New Testament* writing also tells us to remember our bodies are holy dwelling places of God's Living Spirit.[2]

If the people of earlier times knew how interconnected the body and the soul are, why do we seem to forget that fact?

What happens in our inner person does affect our physical health. And poor health or a compromised physical condition, likewise can have a negative impact on our spirit.

With today's fast-paced living, is it any wonder we overlook the little warning signs from our physical body or from within that something isn't in balance? We know that ignoring the shimmy of an auto wheel that's out of alignment can eventually result in problems with our car's steering or suspension systems. Since we're not mechanisms of steel, but flesh and blood, why do we so easily overlook the fact that a disorder in one aspect of our being can set us up for serious problems elsewhere?

What we need first is to understand that we are finely integrated in body and soul. Second, we need an approach to treating disorders and maintaining wellness that takes into account the needs of our whole person, body and soul.

Healthy Body, Healthy Soul is a series of books that takes a "whole person" approach to various health-care issues, with a focus on establishing balance and overall well-being. The goal is to offer a wide range of self-care information and options as you choose how to care for your needs.

Each book offers the best that today's world of complementary health-care therapies has to offer. You'll find that every volume is filled with information on nutrition and diet, herbs and supplements, exercises, and spiritual disciplines—all focused on your specific need. All of it has been reviewed by an advisory board of health-care professionals.

Along with solid information you'll find encouragement and simple, practical steps for making these suggestions part of your daily life. But before you implement any drastic changes to your normal routine, it's advisable that you consult your doctor and make sure you have his or her approval.

Here's to your health—body and soul!

David Hazard
Founder of *The New Nature Institute*

1

What's Eating You?

*I*magine...

- Your boss says the deadline for finishing your project is two weeks sooner than originally planned. And since there's a freeze on hiring, you'll also have to take on a major project left by someone who quit.

- You're shouting at the kids and irritable most of the time. And you don't really know why.

- Your doctor called yesterday. The diagnosis is not good. "Try to relax," he said. "You'll need every bit of energy to fight this."

- Your mechanic calls to say this is a $1200 repair. *Perfect timing.* You've just opened a medical bill and a winter heating bill that made your jaw drop. And the kids need money for school and sports fees.

- You just said yes to *another* volunteer duty. But six household jobs are on hold, and you've agreed to help with your kid's team, and...

- You and your spouse are fighting round 10,000 of the same fight.

- You feel as if you let everyone down most of the time...even God. So many good causes. So little time. So little of you to go around.

Now, let's take a brief personal health self-test. Do any of the following symptoms sound familiar? (Check the statements that apply.)

_____ You wake up after nine hours of sleep still tired. Why are you chronically exhausted?

_____ You've had this headache and this muscle stiffness for…how long?

_____ Your negative thinking has become almost obsessive.

_____ You're feeling down…again.

_____ You're drinking or chain smoking or overeating or procrastinating…again.

_____ Your life feels chaotic, your nerves are on edge, and you're irritable…again.

Who Needs Imagination?

Some of us don't need to imagine scenarios or symptoms like those above, do we? We eat, drink, and breathe stress. We absorb it from the atmosphere we live in every day. Maybe a better way to put it is that stress is absorbing us. We're being eaten alive by it.

Unfortunately, too many of us have accustomed ourselves to living with chronic stress and its effects. As a result, we feel scattered, frustrated, and tense most of the time. We're also plagued by symptoms—minor or major—that tell us our body is suffering from the intensity.

We want life to ease up. We want to feel light, relaxed, free, and at peace. Those are feelings we haven't had for some time. We also want to feel physically healthy again. But instead, we've accepted stress as a "way of life." We've told ourselves that's just the way life is.

Living with stress isn't living, and life wasn't meant to be this way. When we let ourselves become accustomed to stress and accept it as "normal," we've made our first big mistake. We have allowed circumstances to steal from us the well-being we can experience in body, mind, and spirit.

To live with chronic stress is to accept a substitute for living that is little more than an endless effort to keep pressure at bay. It robs us of serenity, destroys the joy of living in the present, and crushes our sense of purpose.

You can get free of stress and reverse its effects on you. You can experience life at a deeper, richer level than ever before.

How? This book presents simple strategies you can use to reverse the effects of stress and restore physical, emotional, mental, and spiritual well-being. We'll look at a wide range of approaches—from the latest nutritional and supplemental approaches…to easy physical techniques for stress relief…to mini vacations and getaways that will ease your body and soul. You'll also discover a simple, adaptable plan for living in a healthy balance that will lead to deep and lasting peace.

In short, this book is packed with practical ideas that will help you not only to escape stress and its damaging effects but also to turn your life around. But before we begin, we need to look at some barriers that will prevent you from taking healthy steps and making important changes.

"I Can Handle It" and Other Barriers to Getting Well

The first and maybe greatest barriers we need to look at are not physical. They exist right between your ears in the form of unhealthy thought patterns. Have you ever asked yourself, "Why do I make room in my life for chronic stress in the first place?" There is a wide range of replies to this question, of course. Among the top answers would be these:

"Life is full of pressure. You just have to get used to it."

As adults, we surely do have to make room for some pressure in our lives. But many of us give in far too much, for too long, and are constantly absorbing more and more pressure from all directions. We bravely tell ourselves, "I can handle it." But what do we get for all our bravery? Sick, tired, and wishing we could escape our own lives.

This may come as a new thought, but we aren't pack mules. Life is not an endurance trial. Sure you *can* handle it, but the question is, *Why?* When we think this way we need to learn that it's okay, even necessary, to off-load sometimes, to let others step in and carry the weight for us.

"I'd rather burn out than rust out."

Those of us who come from backgrounds that place a high value on work, and lots of it, may have heard this line. We may have used it. What does all our high-pressured work do for us? It keeps us two paces ahead of an idea that nips at our heels—that our value is based only on what we can *do*.

Such thinking can be instilled so deeply by hard-working parents, by our culture, even by our religion, that we don't see it for what it is: a life sentence to a prison of restless, driven, unbalanced living.

When we think this way we need to realize that our value is not based on how much we accomplish. Life has depths, colors, and qualities that a hectic work pace can never give us.

"If you want to live up to your potential, you have to push yourself" or "I want so much for my family."

The "human potential" movement of recent years has done a number on way too many of us. It's true each of us has gifts and talents. But who said we're obligated to maximize them all? Whatever happened to making choices and to focus?

We need to recognize that we and other people in our lives do indeed have great potential, but we don't have limitless time, energy, or personal resources. We are finite creatures. As such, we need to seek and establish the balance in which we were designed to live.

"I need to be in control. Other people won't get the job done the way I like it."

Sometimes we know we're going to stress ourselves out by taking charge of everything within a hundred-mile radius. If we had to make a conscious choice—to make our whole being suffer from stress, or suffer a little potential disappointment in the way things turn out—which would we choose?

Sadly, some of us have chosen. Right now we're sacrificing physical, emotional, mental, and spiritual well-being and possibly heading for an early grave because we *insist* on controlling everything. Besides weakening our cardiovascular system, stressing our adrenals, lowering our immunity, and making everyone hate to see us coming, what do we think we're gaining?

"First, I take on way too much stress. Then I experience a crash physically, emotionally, or spiritually. Then I'm okay for a while. It's just the way I am."

Building up to "stress overload," then crashing into sickness, depression, or spiritual deadness is no way to live. For one thing, it's a poor way to manage responsibilities. Inevitably, we let down the people we've (over)committed to.

When we've been riding the roller coaster of stress-bingeing and crashing, we need to tell ourselves that life can be a much smoother, saner, healthier, and ultimately more productive ride than this.

"I owe so much to...my parents...my boss...my community...my church."

These thoughts trap many of us. It's true that we each owe some thanks to other people and to institutions. But that does not mean we're required to sign away the deed to our life. Guilty or obligated thinking erodes our confidence and sense of healthy self-possession— qualities that come when we're free to choose.

When we feel guilty and too obligated, we need to get it straight: Sometimes we're required to challenge unreasonable demands, irritations, unfairness, overbearing habits, and the many other stressors that exist in all relationships. Every healthy relationship is based on each party having the right to say yes...or no.

"Life just keeps dumping more on me" or *"It's all their fault."*

Perhaps the most difficult thought pattern to break through is the one that whispers, "I am a victim of life. There's nothing I can do to change the stressful situation I'm in." We may call it "acceptance" or say we're just "resigned" to it. But mixed in with this line of thinking we almost always find a touch of jealousy that others have it easier, resentment that our load is too great, and maybe just a whiff of self-pity.

When we feel like we're living at the dumping end of life's garbage run, we need to understand something. It's true we can't choose all the circumstances life heaps at us, but we *can* choose how to live, independent of our circumstances. We don't have to live as "victims" of stressful events.

In any case, the minute we begin to negotiate with stress and compromise with it, we get stuck in its web.

Why We Need the Whole-Person Approach

It's possible that, up until now, you haven't really known what to do about the stress in your life. You've accepted it, and you've hated it. It's made you mad or depressed, or perhaps you've worn it like a badge of honor.

Now it's time for a healthy, balanced approach.

This book will help you make some changes that will reduce and manage stress. As with all change, it will take a bit of experimenting to find out what works best for you, along with the development of some new ways of thinking and new habits.

You may be thinking right now, for instance, "Gee, I was hoping to get one or two tips on quick stress relief and get on with my life."

This book is designed so that you can pick and choose the simple stress-relief techniques that will help relieve immediate pressure situations and unpleasant symptoms. But you'll experience the maximum benefit if you take a broader look at your whole life and recognize the truth about your stress-inducing habits and living patterns. In fact, I think you'll agree that taking a whole-life approach is best when you consider what stress does to your entire being.

Some of us are susceptible to taking on more and more stress from our environment. If there's a job to do—be it a physical task or an emotional one—we will take it on as our own. On the job, we take on the tasks of slackers. At home, we take on tasks of emotional and spiritual growth that really belong to our spouses and children. As a result, we take on more and more stress, as if that's the normal thing to do. We turn ourselves into "stress batteries."

Something has to happen with all the energy of the extra pressure we accept. In fact, we internalize it and absorb it into our very being. We hang it on our body—as tension that stresses our nerves, muscles, joints, and organs. We inject it into our chemistry—taxing our hormones, immune systems, and the neurotransmitter chemicals of our brains. We lug it around in our minds in the form of gloomy thoughts that shadow our days and disturb our nights. We let its acid corrode our spirit as a sense of hopelessness or grief or disenchantment with life...maybe even as a distaste for living.

When we don't deal with the effects stress has on our whole person, we invariably allow some aspect of our being to be challenged by stress's demand on our vital energy.

True, stress and pressure can give us a temporary "high" by causing our body to kick-in its quick-start chemicals like adrenaline. We experience a hormonal rush, and we feel "up." We get busy, and for a time it feels good to be energized and handling life's bullying demands. But we quickly deplete our body's store of "instant energy" and go right back to the same habit patterns that induced stress in the first place.

Now our body is that much more depleted. When our first defenses against stress are gone, we're left laboring harder than before. We dip even deeper into the stress "trough," experiencing physical hypertension, the strain or emotional weight of worry, fear, frustration, futility, and anger. We feel more hopeless in spirit, like life is just an endless treadmill.

Is it any wonder we use the term *stressed out?*

"Web of Stress" or "Safety Net of Wellness"?

Even in the midst of a pressured life, we can make choices that create balance, serenity, and well-being for ourselves. There are a variety of single-answer approaches to handling stress. But these usually don't take into account that we are integrated beings. Stress in one area of our life, such as on the job, will affect another part—for instance, our relationships, our health, our spiritual well-being.

We are complex and wonderfully made creatures. We can have every system working at its best for the benefit of our whole person, or stress can spread insidiously throughout our being. On the downside, it's this quick-spreading nature of stress that gives us that stressed-out and scattered feeling, because our body is on high-alert and we're discharging vital energy in all directions.

Therefore, we need to be aware of the ways stress drains our energy, and how it can eventually affect our whole being.

There is a positive flip-side to our beautifully integrated makeup. Just as the negative effects of stress so quickly spread through our whole being, taking a whole-person approach can quickly benefit our whole being as well.

A whole-person approach is important because our personal well-being generates from keeping ourselves in a healthy relationship with the various parts of our life. A sense of calm, serenity, and confidence—as well as health—comes from keeping things in balance. When we feel that all is well, it's because our life is more or less in balance. It's as if our well-being is supported by a "safety net," and there is literally a spring in our step.

It can help to picture the "safety net" or balance we need, with all aspects of our life in order, like this:

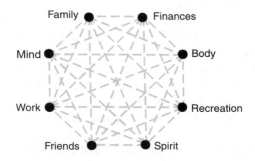

Pressure upsets the balance we need in order to experience health and well-being. Stress in one area invariably spreads to other areas of our life, too. We're left struggling, pushing back against it.

To understand how stress catches us in a web of spreading pressure, it can help to imagine what this looks like. Let's say you're experiencing job stress or a big financial strain. The pressure quickly shoots out to other aspects of your life.

Consider what happens when you're stressed at work. Follow the radiating line that connects work to your friendships. Now be honest with yourself. When you're with a friend whose company you would like to enjoy, how much time do you waste either lost in distracted thinking or verbally grinding over your work problems? Follow the line that connects work to your physical body. Honestly, how often do you experience tension headaches, muscle stiffness, digestive upset, or total depletion during or after a stressful day at work?

Move from work to another aspect of your being—your spirit. When we feel like life is dealing us a tough blow, many of us have serious questions or feel resentful about God. Why are things so unfair? Then there's the connection to family. What will happen to them if you lose your job? What's happening to them now as you drag a heavy load home with you every evening?

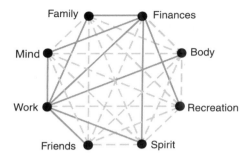

Look again at the picture above and consider how financial pressure can spread throughout your life.

"A moment, please..."

Take a moment for a brief personal stress inventory. It might help to use the "stress web" above to do this. In which areas of your life are you feeling stressed? How does stress in any one area connect to other parts of your life?

For many of us there is usually at least one hidden stress factor that we don't acknowledge or have a hard time seeing. For instance, it's very common to experience spiritual stress. On first glance, we may shrug and say that our relationship with God is at least "okay." By that we mean, "I'm okay with God. And I (think/hope) God is okay with me."

But the spirit is deep, and its spillover into our everyday lives is not always apparent. Because we're caught up in our busy world, we can remain unaware that we have issues with God that contribute to the stress of deep-down and chronic irritation, anger, hopelessness, bitterness, or just cool indifference.

In a later chapter, we'll take some time to do a "spiritual inventory." For now, it can help to stay open to how stress in your spirit may be affecting your whole person. In any case, perhaps you can see more clearly how stress transforms our own nicely integrated being into a struggle against a life-draining web.

On the other hand, imagine that you can make positive changes and transform the web into a safety net of well-being—a way of life that energizes you and fosters good health in every area of your life.

Wouldn't it be great for a change to not feel depleted, but to know you have inner reserves to draw upon?

You can make the changes that will both help you to handle stress and create those inner reserves of strength.

We are creatures of habit, and what we need are new patterns to help us turn stress into serenity and well-being.

So which do you want to have working in your life: a "stress web" or a "safety net of wellness"? Do you really like the old habit patterns which spread and intensify stress? What if you could make simple, practical, and effective changes that would transform you from a suffering "stress battery" into a person who enjoys peace, strength, and good health?

Getting Your Life in Balance

Maybe you don't need any more convincing.

Until now, you may have viewed your stressful situation as "only temporary." Maybe you've been telling yourself, "I just need to get through this job crisis…" or "this divorce." Or "I just need to cut back a little and say *no* more often."

But the fact is, life never throws only one crisis at us. Besides, we all have a knack for turning back *tomorrow* to the very habits we renounced *today* because they were wiping us out *yesterday*. We are creatures of habit, and what we need are new patterns to help us turn stress into serenity.

Throughout this book, we will look at the best new natural methods for reducing and managing stress, including:

- **fast measures you can take in a "stress emergency"**

- **"stress checks" for your work and home environment**

- **the latest facts about stress as it relates to diet and nutrition**

- **finding relief through using herbs and supplements**
- **physical and mental exercises**
- **relaxation techniques**
- **the centering power of prayer and meditation**

All the techniques and discoveries you'll find here are simple, practical, and effective. You'll also find suggestions for creating new habits for stress-free living—little things you can change that will add up to big benefits in your overall health and wellness.

You'll also encounter great quotes, along with many sidebar pieces containing wise advice and useful, interesting tips. These are just to make your day a little lighter!

"Live from a deep place.... We are the artists of our lives."
—THOMAS MOORE

A Center of Peace and Well-being

We don't have to be stressed-out emotionally and scattered spiritually by the strains of life. We can learn to live out of a core of serenity. The secret to peaceful living is knowing this core is not established in a day. Creating a peaceful mind, body, and spirit is something we need for more than the crisis times. In the pages ahead, we'll see how to create the inner peace that will give us strength to carry us through the whole range of life's experiences.

Neither do we have to live with the poor health created by stress in all its forms. We can take advantage of the best discoveries and self-care therapies known today. We can restore our physical health and maintain our personal well-being.

What we need are the right strategies. And we can begin to learn them right now.

2

Make Your Mind Work for You

Stress can make us feel powerless over our own life. Thinking we *are* powerless is an evidence of the mental fogging that occurs when we're under too much pressure. Exactly the opposite is true. We can resolve and manage our stress.

Much of our stress comes from the way we think, and how we mentally process life and its pressuring circumstances. We begin to reverse our problem when we realize that our own mind can work against us…and that we can make it work *for* us.

The Answer Is Not "All Within You," But It's a Great Place to Start

There is a reason we're not looking at stress-reducing supplements and outside interventions first. Those are likely to play roles in helping you reduce and manage stress, and they're covered later. But we are, by and large, a culture that is far too dependent on consuming substances to solve our problems.

Consider our traditional Western medicine—also known as allopathic medicine—and its approach to health. Allopathic medicine relies heavily on the use of prescription medications. And while swallowing a pill can help one system of the body, it can be attacking, stressing, and harming another system at the same time. If you've ever read the warnings and contraindications for most medicines, you understand. They can be terrifying.

In our market-driven culture, many health-food companies and herbal and natural supplement producers seem to have joined in the game. Some companies make steep promises for their product, claiming it will cure allergies, regrow hair, boost sex drive, *and* reverse aging. (And all you wanted was to stop tension headaches!) These marketers are no fools, and they know about the public's demand for a quick solution it can pop in its mouth. And if one substance cures all, that's even better.

And then there's our common obsession with food. We eat for comfort and out of boredom, not for health. Then we eat diet pills, shakes, bars, and prepackaged meals, trying to shed the extra pounds we've packed on.

When it comes to stress, is it any wonder that we just want to reach for a tablet or capsule or a healing tea—something to swallow to help the pressure go away?

Let's be clear. It's quite likely that a drug or herbal or nutritional supplements will be a part of your stress-management strategy. But we must learn not to rely on something we put in our mouth as the main or only piece of our strategy.

It's very important that we recognize two things. First, we need to see the "instant gratification" pill-grab/food-grab for what it can be: a desire to be quickly pacified. Second, it's very human to want to hand off the responsibility for solving a problem to someone else. But resolving the riddle of our personal stress belongs to us and no one else.

The good news is we have some wonderful resources at our command.

One of the greatest God-given gifts we have is at our disposal 24 hours a day. Whether we're attacked by panic in the middle of the night…or overwhelmed daily by too much work, too many bills, too much of life…there it sits, right between our ears. Our *mind* is one of the greatest resources we have for resolving stress.

Right now we may believe we're stuck with our pressures, with no way out. But if we can think, we can always find solutions. And when we know how to gain control of our mental processes, we can use them as allies. We can start on the path to experiencing new depths of calm and confidence.

Three powerful mental strategies we can use are:

- **shifting our focus**
- **shifting from emotional to objective thinking**
- **changing the way we talk to ourselves**

Strategy 1: Shifting Our Focus

If you're looking for an "emergency stress-relief technique," learning how to shift your focus is it! You can use this mental strategy anytime, anywhere. You don't have to "take" anything, and it costs absolutely nothing. Learning this technique supports the old adage that sometimes the simple things are the best.

Stress and intensity go hand in hand. When we're mentally focused, we are actually creating intensity. Perhaps you've been zeroed in on a technical report, or even a heart-pounding drama on television. You'll recall that, at some point, you had to look away, take a breath, and let your shoulders relax. More mental intensity, more stress.

When we're stressed by life, we tend to zoom in on a problem. We turn it over and over in our mind, mentally looking at it from all angles. Without realizing it, our breathing gets shallow, our muscles tense. We're engaged in what's called convergent thinking. All of our attention and energies are being brought to bear. We go round and round in an intense search for a solution or a way out. Our thoughts are so closed to outside input that we can shut out what someone right next to us is saying.

It can help us understand how to use this first stress-relief strategy if we can picture how our mind's focus-power works. Convergent or intense thinking might look like this:

Convergent Thinking

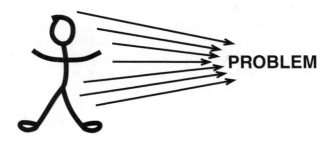

Convergent thinking focuses all our mental, and even some physical, energy intensely on a problem. This gives us a tense, captured-in-a-cage feeling. It's the mind of the wild tiger that's been caught, and now it paces and paws at the trap's door. We're coiled and ready to leap as we look for a way to slip the bolt and spring out of the uncomfortable place we're in. But the door won't yield to our intense focus and helpless pawing, and the energy remains pent up.

Feeling caught with no good way out—this is surely one way to describe stress. To have stress is to have energy that has no good place to go. The uncomfortable place in which we're caught may be temporary, like the trap of a three-mile backup of cars during rush hour. Or it may be chronic, like a schedule that has no letup, the prison of a negative relationship that detracts from our emotions, or the confines of financial overload or illness. Like our lives, our mental focus seems stuck in the intense mode.

Physically, the toll is high. Adrenaline is pumping. Our cardiovascular system tenses, readying us to fight or flee. Our whole being is taxed.

On the other hand, there is another kind of thinking that occurs when we're in a relaxed or serene state. Undoubtedly, you've looked up at a mountain peak, let your eyes wander to the horizon or the expanse of sky. Muscles relax. Breathing slows and deepens. You have a sense of restfulness and well-being.

When we focus "out there" we are, in one sense, stepping out of ourselves mentally, emotionally, and spiritually. We are engaged in what's called divergent thinking. It may help to picture it like this:

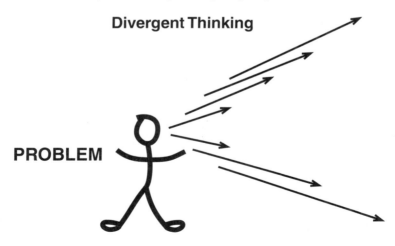

When we can focus outside of and beyond ourselves, we also temporarily step outside our problems and pressures.

The wonderful thing is, we can train ourselves to make the simple switch from convergent and intense thoughts, to divergent and stress-relieving thoughts. We thus become more open to creative ways of thinking that were previously hidden from us.

Before we say more about this, here are the simple steps to divergent thinking:

- **Train your eyes on *distance*—any horizon or the open sky will do.**

- **Breathe in slowly through the nose and fill your chest. Breathe out slowly through the mouth. Allow your breathing to settle into a slow, deep pattern.**

- **Notice if there is muscle tension anywhere in your body. Relax the muscles.**

- **Allow your mind time to rest "out there," beyond yourself.**

- **If stressful thoughts come, gently turn them aside. Set them "behind you" on a "shelf" in your mind, where you can retrieve them later. If your muscles begin to tense, release them.**

The goal of this simple technique is purely to release the pressure of stress. Practice it as long as you need to, until you feel the tension ease. This is pure downtime, and you *need* it!

This technique can be used anywhere. Even as we go about simple "mindless" tasks like gardening or yard work or doing the dishes. As we become adept, it can even be used for a momentary break in the middle of long, intense, and tiring business meetings.

And the effects are almost instant and truly amazing. For one thing, a wonderful chemical change occurs. Our body releases endorphins, those hormones responsible for giving us a sense of peace and well-being. For another, making this shift opens us up to a new mode of thinking. Sometimes we seem to receive guidance and wisdom that comes from outside of our normal thinking processes.

Some people would argue that we are merely allowing our brains a chance to connect up facts and concepts it couldn't piece together while under stress—arranging things in a new order to give us a surprising solution. Others insist that our being opens at a deeper level, allowing us to receive guidance from God—a topic we'll consider more fully in a later chapter.

What's sure is that we have it in our power to use this technique to help us step away from the stress that harms us.

Strategy 2: Shifting from Emotional to Objective Thinking

"I feel so much pressure, I can't even think straight."

"I'm so stressed and so afraid of making a decision because it might be the wrong one."

Have you ever heard yourself say something like this?

Calm thinking helps form a path on which we walk through our situation, whatever it is. Stress erodes that path—that cool, simple logic we use to think, to bring order, and to resolve problems. How? By dumping too many complications and factors on us at once. Or by making us think of huge consequences and outcomes we can't live with.

Let's consider a simple stress situation.

You're under pressure at work. Expenses and bills are growing. You and your spouse or business partner are fighting. Maybe you've just put off handling responsibilities, and now the things you should have taken care of are manhandling you.

Either way, you can think you know what to do at first. But as problems keep circling you think, "Where do I even begin?" You are starting to lose your logical way.

Consider what happens when the situation gets more serious. Let's say we lose a job. Instantly, our head and our heart are both bombarded with many complicated thoughts and feelings. Too many factors loom large all at once, each one tied to an emotion.

We think, "What if I can't find a decent job? What if we get behind in bills, and creditors start to hound us?" (Fear.) "How will I explain why I was let go?" (Shame, guilt…maybe anger.) "We may have to move." (Dread of extra work.) "It could mean pulling the

BACK TO THE PRESENT

Do you need a vacation but can't get away from home? Take a mini vacation.

Maybe you remember being a kid and lounging on your back under the shade of a tree. Or just staring up at a blue sky adrift with clouds, or watching for shooting stars at night. Your mind was out of gear and free to fly.

Stress pulls us out of the present moment, and so it blinds us to the simple wonders that are in each moment.

Want to recapture those relatively carefree days, at least for an hour or two? Here's what you do:

- *Tell everyone you're taking a mini vacation.* Here's your line: "I'm not here for the next hour."

- *Find a spot to lounge.* In cold weather, an overstuffed chair or sofa by a window will do. In warm weather, take a blanket to the yard or a park...better still, a riverbank, where the sound of moving water adds to the tranquil ambience.

- *Resist the urge to bring a book.*

- *Leave your cares at home.* For some people, it helps to dash off a list of things that might plague you so you can tell yourself, "Now I can relax, knowing I won't forget these important things. But they'll have to wait."

- *Study the shapes of natural things.* As a stressed-out culture, we tend to miss out on the soul-restorative glory of creation: the thistle-pink and wolf-gray of an evening sky, the artistic curve of a branch.

- *Before you return home, you might think about this:* Beauty is always present in the world. And the beauty of living things lies partly in the fact that they can come in such odd shapes and colors. You might consider your life in light of this simple truth. Or you might just drowse into a much-needed nap.

kids from school and friends and uprooting us all." (Grief.) "Vacations and household upgrades will have to be put off indefinitely." (Sadness and disappointment.)

Let's say the emotional pitch of your problems is higher. Maybe a spouse or child is seriously ill. Much tougher. The fear is more acute, the potential loss more severe, the needs more pronounced.

Stress has heaped a barbed tangle of issues and emotions right in the middle of our path. What do we do *now?* What do we do *next?*

Restoring mental balance and well-being comes when we practice objectivity. This we can do with four simple steps.

Step 1—Step Out

In a ball game, a referee's job is to be sure the game is moving along the way it's meant to·be played. That requires the ref to step back from the field of play, keep an eye on the big picture, and keep things in order. When things get too chaotic, the ref stops the game and sorts out the problems.

Every one of us is a player caught up in the game of our own life. We're stuck in the push and shove of events. We also get caught up emotionally and spiritually over what we think is fair and unfair. That's when the chaos of the game *outside* moves *inside.* We lose our sense of order, and logical thinking goes. We lose our perspective and we lose our calm.

Sometimes we need to step out from our position in the events, and get the broader view again. In fact, we need to do this often. We may need to step back for an hour, an afternoon, a whole day, or a whole weekend to get the break in time we need. Only then can we sort out the chaotic events and interior issues pressuring us.

Do you have a secluded cabin where you can get away? A retreat center or monastery? A favorite park or footpath? (How about that mini vacation?) Anyplace where you can get away, be alone, and purposely relax will do.

Just being away and alone can feel good enough. But there's a purpose to this getaway. We're asking for our inner life to be sorted out, and for peace to return with that order.

In any case, the minute we move ourselves out of the chaos, we've begun to relieve stress.

Step 2—Assess

What we're doing when we step out of life's normal flow is giving ourselves relaxed space in which to assess.

Let's follow the example of a referee. When a ref halts play, it's to take stock of some aspect of the game that's out of control.

Sometimes we *think* we know exactly what the problem is. But think again about the webbed interconnection that goes on inside us. We do well to step back and see the bigger context and to let all parts of our life "speak."

Frank liked his job, but was sure the stress he felt was coming from his boss. Taking a day off to assess, he realized he had put himself under pressure by taking on a civic club project *and* a fundraiser for the country club. When his boss needed some overtime work, Frank blamed him for the resulting pressure. He attributed his angry outbursts at his family to "that stupid guy I work for."

When Frank took an afternoon to assess his situation, he realized his back ached, his head was pounding, and he felt drained inside. He also realized his frustration was misdirected, and that as long as he blamed someone else he was indeed powerless to take care of himself, his real needs, or his family.

Sometimes our stress comes from minimizing a problem when we need to be more honest and admit how much it affects us. Joan hated whining and self-pity, and her standard line was, "It's no big deal." But a string of events brought a lot of stress, and Joan began to shed weight rapidly and lose her hair.

When she was honest, Joan had to admit all the stress she had ignored had added up to a health problem that *was* a big deal.

Sometimes, too, we need to assess our actual ability to handle a situation, as opposed to pretending we're handling it well. Louis prided himself on being a competent, capable guy. He took on more and more responsibilities at home, at work, at church, and in his daughter's softball league—heaping stress upon stress—never recognizing stress as the source of the depression and terrible fatigue that overtook him.

Stepping out of the situation gives us time to reflect and examine things, and it gives our mind a chance to free itself of emotional clouds so we can get a clearer picture of reality.

Take a moment now and assess your situation.

Do You Feel Stress from One or More of These Sources?

(check spaces that apply)

_____ Overload at work
_____ Overload at home
_____ Carrying negative or painful emotions
_____ Feeling criticized, blamed, or underappreciated
_____ Bearing too much responsibility for other
people's lives and well-being
_____ Health concerns
_____ Chaotic schedule or surroundings
_____ Poor mental habits; allowing for too many distractions
_____ Spiritual distress like guilt, hopelessness,
lack of purpose or meaning
_____ Feeling ashamed, as if you are somehow "defective"

One of the best things we can do is to make an honest assessment of our lives. Have we had a part in allowing things to become the way they are? If not, what part can we play in resolving the tension and restoring serenity?

Step 3—Do Your Part

The other part of assessment is to determine what you can do to resolve stress and regain peace. We are talking about determining what *you* can do—and you alone. This is not as easy as it seems.

Determining our part in resolving stress turns our vital energies in a positive direction. It focuses those energies on moving ahead instead of leaving us in a "stuck" mode. It begins to restore drive, forward momentum, and a calming sense of order.

Determining what we can do can be as simple as buying a pocket calendar or reorganizing our office or home filing system. Or it may be recognizing that we fly off the handle or blame others or criticize too quickly...and finding a different, healthier outlet for our emotions.

Assessing our part may also take more courage than we knew we had. We may need to recognize that a problem is not solvable. Or we may determine it's beyond our means to handle and that we need experienced help. (More on this in a moment.)

For six years, Dan worked for a man whose pattern was to set the whole office working on a project, only to then change his mind. One week from the completion date, the boss would change directions on a whim. Over and over, time, effort, and money were wasted. Workers lost their sense of purpose. Stress ran high.

Dan made many attempts to get the man to see the chaos and stress he left in his wake. Nothing worked. And after laboring to help bring about change, Dan felt even more stressed.

Finally, his wife offered a piece of honest assessment Dan had overlooked. "Your boss is either a weak or unhealthy man. But the longer you work for him, and the more you try to change him, the weaker and more unhealthy *you* are becoming."

Dan had indeed been giving up the one and only power we all have by trying to change his boss. He could not solve the problem of his boss's terrible management style. He had forgotten that the only person he had the power to change was himself.

When Dan realized this, he was able to refocus on the actions that were within his power. This meant assessing the situation clearly. His boss was not about to leave, and upper management seemed oblivious to the problem. And since Dan could not tolerate the situation, he began looking for a new job. Though it took time and effort, he landed in a less stressful, more rewarding position.

Step 4—Letting Others Do Their Part

When we step back and honestly assess our stressful situations, we also give ourselves a chance to recognize this great truth: Some work is not ours to do.

Sometimes we discover the change we need to make is small and simple. Rather than being the household slave and overtaxing ourselves, we may need to train and discipline our children to do their chores.

We may need to let a person we love wrestle with a conflict without our constant help and intervention. In this way, other people can learn to bear the weight of life, to make mistakes, to succeed, and to make mature decisions.

Carl was everybody's "go to" guy. "Can do, will do" was his motto. He carried the ball for his wife, kids, friends, and many people in his church. He had no idea how much stress he was carrying until a minor incident with his heart gave him a warning. Carl realized he probably hadn't done others as much good as if he had given support and advice and stepped back and let them achieve success under their own steam.

Allowing others to shoulder the weight of their own responsibilities is right because it restores balance in relationships. Along with that, it eases stress by taking undue pressure off us.

Another great truth we need to learn is this: Easing stress that's too big for us to carry comes as we learn how to "relax into" others when necessary.

When we find that stress is unbearable or that responsibilities are too great, we need to learn the age-old secret of "letting go." This we do by temporarily handing the weight of knowing and giving direction to others who are better equipped—such as professionals and counselors—while we relax and accept their wisdom and guidance. Our part is to keep seeking help until we're fully satisfied it's the right help we need.

Jane was living under tremendous financial pressure until a friend directed her to one of the many free financial services available through banks, lending institutions, and county and state governments. Ron was overburdened by marriage problems and a child who was in and out of trouble. Thinking it over, he realized there were resources available to his family through local churches and counseling services. Relying on others relieves stress when we're not fully equipped to help ourselves.

Remaining objective when our every emotion wants to drag us into confusion and stress takes practice. But as we learn these simple mental strategies, we'll discover how being objective opens us up to creative options, restores calm, and adds to our well-being.

℞

Two "Gift Thoughts" in a Box

∿

It's doubtful there is anyone on the planet who doesn't need to learn what it means to let go and relax more effectively. We all need to learn how to assess when things are too big, too far beyond our control for us to handle. It's then that we can learn how to "let go" on a more profound and spiritual level and relax into God.

This is an important topic that will be discussed in a later chapter on spiritual strategies for managing stress. For now, consider this: When you have faith you will still experience stress, but you never have to carry the weight alone.

Some of us never learn how to practice healthy objectivity, and we stay stuck in the trap of mental stress for one reason: We drive ourselves crazy trying to make perfect choices, or choices that will be the best for everyone. As thinking adults we need to settle down to this fact: *Our choices will not be perfect.*

Even with the best guidance, we will rarely choose a course that makes everyone happy or the solution that will satisfy all our needs. Thinking we *can* make perfect choices is a source of great stress and defies the reality of living in an imperfect world.

We can achieve a healthy balance when circumstances are beyond us by leaving perfection to God.

Strategy 3: Changing the Way We Talk to Ourselves

We would swear under oath that our stress is all external, caused by pressuring circumstances and people. It's true the *triggers* of stress come from without. But the truth is we make an event stressful—or at least add to it—by the way we respond from within.

How? One of the biggest contributing factors is our *self-talk.*

Self-talk is that interior monologue we carry on all the time, mostly without even realizing it. This running commentary is constantly evaluating, comparing, sizing up, criticizing, judging.

Self-talk is based on our deepest beliefs—those "doctrines" and laws of the soul. It's the voice that tells us how to feel and act, and what to say in response to every situation.

This voice is as individual as we are. For that reason, no two people will respond exactly alike to the same circumstance.

Let's say two people are diagnosed with the same severe illness.

One person may have a deep religious faith and a stable family on which she bases her life. Her self-talk may go like this: "I don't like this. I guess this is the time to count on God's help. And I know I've got the support of my husband and kids. Bad as this is, I'll get through it somehow." Her stress level is moderate.

The other is the sole support of three children, and she has not invested as much in developing a spiritual life. Her self-talk may go like this: "This is a nightmare. I'm so furious and I'm not sure who to be mad at....And what if I can't take care of the kids? We're headed for disaster." Her stress level is understandably off the charts, further compromising her health.

As you can see, it makes a big difference how we interpret events and what we tell ourselves about them. One person is far more disposed to releasing stress and experiencing peace and wellness than the other.

We don't alter reality, create wealth, cure illness, or change our boss just by using the right words or thoughts. To have that kind of power on the tip of our tongue would be nice, but it's not so. Neither are we to blame for "bringing problems on ourselves" if we have a tendency to be gloomy and speak negatively.

Nor can we drum up a cheerful, stress-free disposition just by repeating positive thoughts and words. Empty words—no matter how positive, while in the center of our being a red disaster siren is sounding—just won't do it. For that reason, we'll need to discuss core beliefs more in a later chapter, too.

Nonetheless we can contribute to restoring calm, and experience wellness by tuning in to our inner monologue and learning how to change it.

Here are three ways we can reduce stress that's generated by our self-talk.

1. *Change the way we talk to ourselves about other people.*

First, many of us create stress for ourselves by thinking we are too needed.

A child spills a glass of milk, a friend has a problem, a coworker wants extra time off, and we tell ourselves, "They need my help. I have to step in." Soon we're doing our job and theirs, too. This overloads us and doesn't give them a chance to rely on their own resources or to find help apart from us.

We can take the pressure off by telling ourselves, "They'll benefit by struggling a little and doing it on their own" or "Letting them rely solely on me isn't good. They need to find others who can help, too."

Second, we sometimes generate stress in relationships by being too critical. We may think it's "those incompetents" all around us. No one "does it right." The truth may be that we're too perfectionistic. Or it may be that a person hasn't been trained. Or they may really be incompetent! Hacking away at them in our self-talk only harms us and does nothing to help.

Quit raising your blood pressure by telling yourself, "He's a jerk who can't handle the job." Instead, tell yourself, "Okay, so he's not cutting it, but he's probably doing the best he can."

Third, we can generate stress by telling ourselves no one gives us what we need. We constantly remind ourselves that they don't support, praise, or reward us in the way we deserve.

The truth is, most of us need a far more realistic view of humanity and of what we can expect from others. We can benefit by learning how to cope when other people let us down.

We tell ourselves, "If I have to ask for help or encouragement it's not worth it. They should offer it without being asked." We would be far better off saying, "No one knows what I need if I don't speak up. If I stay silent, they'll think everything's fine the way it is."

Or we think, "I spoke up and made my needs clear. Now I'll just sit and watch and see if they make the right move." Instead of playing the part of a spider waiting for a fly, far better to think, "I'll check to see if they understood what I asked for, to see if they're willing and able to do it."

Fourth, we create stress by continuing to ask for something the other person isn't willing or able to give.

It's said that insanity is doing the same thing over and over and expecting a different response. Some of us do that when we continue to seek support from someone who is not likely to give it. That is a sure formula for stress.

We tell ourselves, "Maybe this time she'll understand." Or "Maybe today he'll give me what I need." Or we say, "Why am I so unfortunate to be stuck with such a heartless person for a friend?"

We relieve stress (and probably a good measure of self-pity) when we tell ourselves instead, "For some reason, this person is not able right now to give me what I need. I'll free them and free myself from the unhealthy pressure of making this same demand of them over and over. I'll move on and accept support and help from someone else."

2. Change the way we talk to ourselves about life's tough events.

Politicians have made "spin" an art form. They're always telling us how to interpret events. We could learn a lesson here.

How we *think* about life's hard knocks can actually determine their impact on us more than the events themselves.

A serious illness strikes. We lose someone we love. We can tell ourselves, "This is terrible. I can't live with this pain and tragedy." Or we can acknowledge the truth: "Tragedy and loss are part of living. I need to figure out how to adjust my life to this and go on."

A child is in turmoil or lands in serious trouble. We can tell ourselves, "I'm a terrible parent" or "My child is a mess." Or we can say, "Lots of people get off to a rough start. I love my child, and I'll continue to do my best to help him—imperfect as that may be."

We're betrayed by a spouse, a friend, a company, or a group to whom we've been loyal. We can torment ourselves, saying, "I would never treat anyone this way. I'll never trust anyone again." Or we can generate a more mature response, telling ourselves, "People can be weak and act in very disappointing ways. They won't always treat you the way that makes you feel valued or that honors your loyalty to them."

3. Change the way you talk to yourself about yourself.

Some of us spend most of our waking hours locked in combat with huge attacks against our very person. The enemy is none other than *us*. Here are just a few examples of negative, even destructive self-talk that may be causing you stress.

"What a terrible [parent, worker, business partner] I am." Many of us stress ourselves with self-accusations and self-punishment. Better to replace these statements with the honest truth: "I make mistakes. I'm human. But there's grace in this universe, and that means I can keep learning and try to do better next time."

"[So and so] is much better at this. I don't have what it takes. And I never will." Hard self-evaluations don't really take the pressure off. Comparing ourselves to other people who seem capable and happy only grinds us in the dust. Life is about finding out who we are, what we like, and what we're good at. We can say instead, "I might learn a lot about myself if I attempt this. At least I'll find out if I like it and if I'm good at it. If not, I can drop it and go on to something else."

"I need to do this by myself. Asking for help is weak, a sign of incompetence" or "I can't tell anyone about…." When we're too independent or too secretive, we wind up carrying too many of life's heavy burdens alone. Far better to open ourselves to the give-and-take of caring, health giving friendships. We can tell ourselves, "Helping each other and trusting people is what creates friendships. And good friends are a part of what makes life worth living."

"I knew better and I still blew it. What a stupid, stupid, stupid person I am." Such thinking can betray a legalistic mindset, one that whispers at a deep level, "Make a mistake and it's all over for you."

"I wanted to say *no*, but I said *yes*. What's the matter with me? Why did I let them force me into this?" This monologue is riddled with blame toward ourselves and toward others. The questions we might better ask are, "Why do I feel guilty saying no?" or "Why do I need to appear so agreeable?" And instead of adding inner pressure to the mix, we can tell ourselves, "I gave in this time. But it's the last time. Next time all I need to tell them is, 'I really can't.' Period."

"Whatever the mind can conceive, man can achieve." The guy who said this was probably stretching it a bit. Nonetheless, we can use the 48-ounce mass of gray matter we've been given to begin resolving stress and move toward balance and well-being. Use your head. Mom and Dad said it. It's still good advice.

"SOMETHING TO CLEANSE THE PALATE?"

Want to try something that refreshes the soul?

Try "cleansing the inner palate" by declaring a "fast" on negative self-talk. Just for a day, try catching yourself every time your inner monologue comes up with something critical, sarcastic, and superior...or self-pitying or self-accusing.

When you do, gently push it aside. Remind yourself that fasting from negative self-talk "unclogs" the inner person. You become freer inside and more open to positive, creative ways to see people and events. You may like it and make it a way of life!

James in his epistle exhorted the early Christians to "control the tongue," and perhaps that includes controlling what we say to ourselves.

If you learn this particular discipline you'll become easier to live with—for you and everyone around you, too! You will also be more upbeat and relaxed...and ultimately healthier.

3

Stress and Your Spirit

A thousand authors would probably come up with ten thousand definitions for the spirit and what it is. For the purposes of this book, we'll talk about spirit as the core part of us that holds our deepest beliefs and life values.

In fact, for the purposes of this book, we want to talk about stress's impact on the spirit instead of its effect on the emotions. Why this approach?

Because psychology has made great strides in recent decades, we tend to focus on our emotions—on how things make us feel. But our spirit is more than our feelings; it is the central essence of our being. Thomas Moore refers to it as that "deep and eternal person...God-given...one's original core." [3] In the Psalms, David refers to it as the "inmost being." By that he means the "life-flame" of our unique personhood, which his son Solomon later called the "candle of the Lord." This gives us a wonderful picture of our inner being as a sort of "living flame," the "true me" and "true you" ignited into being by the breath of God. [4] Philosopher Abraham Heschel calls it the place where we "commune with reality"[5] in the most ultimate sense.

We Are Not Machines

Contemporary science and all its "children"—including allopathic (traditional) medicine, nutrition, and other health-related disciplines—look at the body as if it were a machine. Oddly enough, they tend to ignore the all-important spark that makes the body *not* a machine.

The spirit within us is this spark of life itself. It is the deepest source of our vitality and well-being...or lack of it. Because stress in our spirit can be buried deep inside, it's not always easy to make the connection between surface symptoms and the underlying source.

Here is a partial list of symptoms that can indicate when a stressed spirit may be compromising our well-being.

- *Troubled sleep,* bad dreams

- *Constant fears*—specific concerns, like fear of losing a spouse, a child, or our own life

- *Anxiety*—a general feeling that "something terrible is about to happen"

- *Relational distress*—arguing, retreating, isolating ourselves

- *A compromised immune system*—indicated by constant colds or infections or by flare-ups of rheumatoid arthritis, fibromyalgia, lupus, and other immune disorders

- *Gastrointestinal disorders* with no biological source

- *Chronic headaches*

- *Muscle aches* and soreness

- *Skin disorders*—eczema, unexplained rashes

- *Paranoia*—second-guessing others' motives, a feeling that you're being "set up" for a fall

- *Panic attacks*—the sudden onset of terror, accompanied by rushing heart rate, shaking, sweats, and overall weakness

When we experience such symptoms, we may find there is a connection with inner-core tensions such as:

- *Insecurity*—a chronic fear of being left on our own when we are vulnerable and need help

- *Guilt*—a conviction that we've "broken a code," either that of our religion or principles we hold strongly

- *Buried anger*—a desire to punish someone—God or others—for harming or letting us down

- *Distrust or suspicion*—a feeling of estrangement or alienation—from God or others that goes beyond healthy self-reliance

- *Shame*—a sense we are "defective" or out of the norm as other people have defined "normal"

- *Rejection*—a sense that we are not acceptable as we are

Not incidentally, it's the spirit that also carries our strongest-held beliefs about God and living. It also tells us how to interpret the events of life and how to understand ourselves and other people. It directs us in the way we are to go, or tells us we have strayed off the path we should be on.

That is to say, it's our spirit that actually "counsels" us in how to respond to these things, and for that reason it actually directs our emotions. At the same time, whether we have a peaceful or a troubled spirit can greatly influence our health and well-being.

Experience Tells Me...

For some of us, it's hard to be honest about the fact that, as good as we are at holding it all together on the outside, stress is eating us alive from somewhere deep within.

Personally, I wasn't very honest with myself at a time when stress was crushing the life out of me. In part, this had to do with the fact that I needed to see myself as a strong, "put-together" person. In part, it also had to do with the fact that I thought I had all the answers to life's conflicts and questions.

I am of the Christian faith. I came to this faith first by being born into a Christian family, then later by personal conviction and commitment. In a very gung ho, all-out way, as a teenager I tucked a black leather-covered Bible under my arm and committed myself to following Jesus Christ.

For a long time my spiritual life consisted of gathering a lot of head knowledge. I learned the doctrines of the faith, studied systematic theology, and took on logical ways of thinking about such things as the state of the world and the means of salvation. I also developed staunch opinions about the ethics of practical living, public policy, and political matters.

Frankly, in certain ways this helped me. It gave me a solid set of beliefs and a sure hope as I faced a relativistic and often despairing world. It gave me the impetus to take care of my physical body and kept me out of drug and alcohol abuse. It also helped me avoid the narcissism of adolescence by giving me a desire to understand and help other people.

Yet a number of years after my initial gung ho experiences, something was clearly amiss. Outwardly, my life was well-ordered. But inwardly, it was as if I was twisting on a rope. My mind was often in turmoil with unanswered questions. My emotions ranged from flat to overwrought. I felt good about myself or terrible about myself, depending on my "spiritual performance record."

Then, over a period of months, interior tensions triggered symptoms in my physical body. First, I was unable to sleep well at night and had trouble concentrating on my work during the day. Then I was racked with periodic fevers and a weakness that put me in bed for days at a time. Eventually, pain grew from a dull ache to burning in all my joints. Doctors diagnosed an autoimmune disease, prescribed powerful drugs, and said that in time I would need joint-replacement surgeries.

Eventually, I found a way out of this terrible, physical predicament. One of the cornerstones of my "treatment plan" was learning how to deal with the interior stresses that were plaguing my spirit.

In part, I realized that I was experiencing core-level stresses generated by trying to live within the grid of a set "belief system." My head knowledge didn't seem to relate to my innermost being. I also discovered that I hadn't been given a very good set of "spiritual tools" to help me deal with my personal inner needs, with the ups and downs of life, or with other human beings as I struggled to relate to them. The set of beliefs in my head didn't help me understand and manage the realities of living.

Today, I still hold to Christian beliefs. But because of my physical meltdown, I've learned something. My well-being was compromised by an inner stress that people with strong beliefs of any kind can encounter. It doesn't matter if the belief system is an actual religion, a set of business or ethical principles, or a strict adherence to a rigid set of personal goals. Eventually you're likely to encounter the same problem: Living by doctrines or by principles alone makes you inwardly inflexible, out of balance, and unwell. Spiritual arthritis sets in, and if you're not careful, even spiritual rigor mortis.

I believe there is a basic truth here, and it's this: Practically speaking, it doesn't matter if we have an orderly set of beliefs, all labeled and shelved neatly in our head. Our spirit is not fooled. Deep down we recognize when things are in disarray. Turmoil, confusion, sadness, depression, and isolation from other people is the witness something is wrong. At some point, we will either learn to go deep, to the level of the spirit, and learn how to experience true health there, or we will go on to live very unhealthy (and often secretive) lives characterized by:

- lack of peace

- unhappiness, emotional emptiness, and even despair

- a flat or dull outlook on life due to a lack of a healthy mental/philosophical "quest"

- a string of disappointing, even broken relationships, due to judgments that cut us off from other people

- a sense of isolation from humanity in general

- poor physical health as a result of the heavy, unhappy, disgruntled, or conflicted spirit that keeps us stressed at the deepest level of our being

An effective strategy that has worked for many people has been the rediscovery of ancient spiritual disciplines such as prayer, silence, and simplicity. These practices come from the deep, old, and wonderful wellspring of Judeo-Christian spirituality, which is rich in wisdom about the care and well-being of the human spirit.

Today, many spiritual and alternative-health gurus talk about stress relief and finding inner peace. They discuss techniques, but often neglect the need to face *all* the issues that can trigger tension in our inner being. For instance, if we're feeling stress because we've violated a code, then taking vitamins and resorting to aromatherapy or massages will give some relaxation, but they won't get at the real problem. Neither will trying to re-program our thoughts by revising the code.

In Christian spirituality, we find several strategies necessary for healthy spiritual living. I highly recommend these strategies to you.

Strategy 1: Examining Core Beliefs

In truth, a lot of stress-energy is generated by the core beliefs that drive us. These are beliefs we hold deeply inside, at such a deep level that we may not even know we have them. They may be related to our religious persuasion, or just to strongly held principles.

Our core beliefs may include beliefs about life and the tasks that are ours to do. If we listen carefully, we may sift our true core beliefs from the things we say, such as:

- "It's all up to me. Even though there are people who could help, they won't. I'm on my own with all this work to do. And it does no good to ask. You have to do it all yourself."

- "If I don't do such and such, then something terrible will happen. Someone will be hurt or let down. Something big will fall through. And I couldn't accept that."

- "There is absolutely no one else who can do this the right way. I have to do it, because if someone else does it the results won't be as good. And I couldn't tolerate that."

We may also be suffering stress from core beliefs about who and what we are. Have you ever thought or said:

- "Because I have (a certain illness, upbringing, personality, or physical look) I'm not lovable...not even likable. I'm a lesser human being."

- "I'm not like other people in the things I think and the things I like. I'm not normal. As people go, I'm just weird...defective."

- "I did something wrong and it can never be made right again. No one can forgive me. I'm a terrible, terrible person."

Deepest of all are our beliefs about our relationship to God. These beliefs can help or hinder us as we go through a stressful time in life. Trust in God is meant to be a vital tool to help us through a time of crisis. But too often our erroneous core beliefs about God cause us stress deep in our being.

How can we know whether our perceptions of God are harmful? They will generally voice themselves, when we are open and honest, like this:

- "This is punishment. God is paying me back for what I did wrong."

- "This is a trial. I'm being tested to see if I'm worthy. I just have to bear it."

- "Just when I need help, I'm abandoned. I can't even count on God."

- "The life I've been given (or the circumstances I've been dealt) are just not fair. God plays favorites, and I'm not one of them."

One piece of great wisdom from the biblical writer Solomon tells us, "As [a man] thinketh in his heart, so is he."[6] The thing about core beliefs is that they lie deep in the substrata of our thinking. Often these powerful declarations of what we believe to be true are all but hidden even from us. Nevertheless, they can stress us and drain us of our vitality.

Often our core beliefs don't surface until we're under incredible pressure and something in our life activates the "stress web." Sometimes it's only then that we make connections between our core beliefs and surface symptoms. Only then do we discover the hidden sources of a negative energy that's worked against us for years.

Leslie contracted polio when she was four. While growing up she heard people refer to her as "the crippled girl." In her teens and young adult years, males rejected her. When other pressures came—in her career, with her finances—they triggered distress deep in her spirit, too.

Leslie began to isolate herself from friends because it was too hard to hear them discuss their active social lives. Alone, her thoughts were dominated by questions like, "Why is my life so hard?" and "Why did this happen to me?"

Leslie eventually realized that deep down she had felt abandoned most of her life. Loving as her family had been, no one could understand the desolation and emptiness of a little girl who could not be "just like the other girls" or play as they did. She felt that if there was a God, He just didn't care about her tragedy.

Until Leslie learned how to counter the destructive power of her erroneous core beliefs she was prey to their negative impact.

Tom and his young wife, Julie, were both in grad school when she became pregnant. For personal reasons they decided to terminate the pregnancy. Some years later, after the birth of their first son, Tom began to ride an emotional roller coaster. In the changing economy, Tom's job suddenly seemed in jeopardy. Rather than adapting, Tom plunged into depression over the thought that he could lose his job.

Soon, Tom was contracting one cold after another. His muscles were constantly stiff and sore. He experienced fevers and swollen glands as stress severely compromised his immune system.

The fact that he seemed to carry a deep fear that his young son would be lost or killed was a signal to the counselor Tom was seeing. Eventually, his deep core beliefs surfaced.

"A lot of stuff went on inside me after Jason was born," says Tom. "I realized I didn't take much thought for the life of the first child that was given to us. As a man I'm supposed to be a protector and provider. So I guess I believe I'm going to be punished. Maybe Jason will be taken from me. Or I won't be able to provide. The odd thing is, I don't think about God as a punishing God. I had no religious upbringing at all. It's got to be something instinctive."

Tom faced the fact that he had always felt it was wrong to terminate Julie's pregnancy for his own convenience. He had felt this even though he wasn't a "religious" person at the time. Working with a counselor, he resolved the guilt he had been carrying at a very deep level.

Like Leslie, Tom had to learn how to examine his core beliefs, recognize when they were destructive, and replace them with healthier and more accurate beliefs. Both did so by using strategies like these that follow.

Strategy 2: Spiritual Attitude Adjustment

Many of us stress out because our view of things is out of alignment with reality. Because of that, our attitude—that is, our approach to life—is also out of whack.

If we're honest, most of us believe something is seriously wrong with the way the world is being run. Sometimes we may also think that there's something seriously wrong with pretty much everyone in the world. Maybe there is even something wrong with God.

When we think this way, we need a spiritual attitude adjustment. Christian wisdom teaches us that:

God is God, and we are not.

For many of us, the problem is that we think we have it all figured out. Our system of religious beliefs or principled thinking tells us that if we just live in a certain way, things will generally go right for us. We translate that to mean, "If I believe this, and if I do that, and if I can get other people to do it 'the right way,' life will run the way I think it should run."

This kind of thinking allows us to play into the hands of our old controlling nature. To insist that we have all the answers (or most of them, anyway), and to pressure the world and others in our world to "think" like us and "do" like us, is to step into the place of God. When the universe and other people don't do things "our way," we are left frustrated and angry.

Christian spirituality teaches us humility. Humility simply means knowing our limited place in the great order of things. We are to remember that God is God, and we are not. Because we are *not* God, we aren't capable of knowing all things. We aren't capable of judging other people. Our most productive role in the scheme of things is to face ourselves honestly and to speak up for the truths we have learned.

The world will one day be a safe place again and a fair place, but not right now.

Some of our stress comes from fear. What if our beloved child or spouse is killed, abducted, or lost to us? What if we get a terrible illness? Another type of stress comes from the sense that things are not "fair." Evil people get away with so much. We never get the breaks that other people get. We do well to recognize that this is a world in which unfair things happen to good people. In fact, to all of us.

Christian spirituality teaches us that right now the world is disordered. On a grand scale, something is deeply out of whack here. Too often justice will not prevail. Not right now. Awful things happen to innocent people. To every one of us, Jesus says that the rain falls on the good and the evil alike.[7]

In short, we do well to adopt an attitude of acceptance. Life for now is the way it is. We stress ourselves by insisting things are "unfair" and "shouldn't be this way." We create sickness-inducing turmoil by focusing on things we can't change. Things *are* unfair, things are "iffy"—for now. Yes, some of us do seem to have it tougher than others. But we don't have to allow ourselves to get hung up over "cosmic injustice." Why everything happens as it does is not within our capacity to know.

In the end, we can let go of our demand for fair play and learn how to make the very best of the circumstances we've been given. To do so is to allow a deep calm to fill our innermost being—what the scriptures refer to as the "peace of God." And this inevitably works to promote our total well-being.

For those of us with strong beliefs, that means learning how to surrender our lives more completely to God. That may mean recognizing we have entrusted certain aspects of our life to God's care, but we never before have entrusted *this* part. It often means recognizing we are too deeply attached to something or someone. We need another attitude adjustment.

Let people be just people. Let things be just things.

Sometimes we're stressed from playing God in other people's lives. We forget we're just men and women like everyone else, somewhere on a learning and growth curve. Yet often it seems we insist that other people live according to our opinions and judgments. We learned by experience, but we don't allow others the freedom to have their own learning experiences and mistakes. We pressure, manipulate, control.

At the other extreme, sometimes we foolishly let other people take the place of God in our lives. We're terrified that they will leave us or disappoint us or fail to be "perfect" in our eyes. We depend on their constant presence and assurance, and sometimes on their perfect behavior, in a way that can only be described as idolatry.

We let go of stress and restore peace when we take the attitude that only God is God. Only God is perfect, unfailing, ever-present, and never-leaving. People, possessions, positions—everything that is not God—is only temporary. They are as subject to change and demise as we are. And the reason they are taken out of our lives, and the timing of that, is known only to God.

To accept the fact that people and things come and go is to accept the nature of things. Yes, it may be sad at first. But taking this attitude soon builds in us a sense of healthy detachment. We *enjoy* people and things, but we don't *need* them. That's because we are no longer dependent on people or things as the source of our well-being. We find ourselves at peace, free to accept them as gifts. We know they are as likely to go *from* us as they were to come *to* us. We become grateful for them. We no longer need to control them, and so we free them from the stress of our demands and disapprovals.

What is lost will one day be restored. What is unfair will one day be made fair.

Many people experience deep-level stress from living without hope. The permanent address of their innermost being is P.O. Box 1, Things Are Bad and Going to Get Worse.

Christian spirituality teaches us that our peace lies in the hope of a promised new creation. It gives us the attitude of happy expectancy. Awaiting the time when God will "make all things new"[8] is anything but escapist thinking. It does not teach us to become passive, giving up on the world or ignoring the wrong in it. Rather, it gives us the peace and wise perspective that comes from knowing that all our small efforts now will be rewarded one day when we see "all things made new" and all wrongs righted.

What I've described throughout this strategy are the attitudes of acceptance. Acceptance does not mean giving up and accepting the status quo. Instead, we accept the big scheme of things, and then accept that we have a small but important part to play in it.

Many of us feel stressed inside because we are out of sync with our place in the big order of things. Witness the fact that so many of us say, "I wish I knew my purpose for being here," or "I wish I knew what I was going to be when I grow up."

Perhaps it is time—whether you have a devout faith or are just discovering one—for you to move from stress to peace. You can do so by adopting the attitudes that restore us to peace and purpose.

Strategy 3: Confession—Taking Rightful Responsibility

Many of us live with a sense that there is a code of conduct we need to live by. And a great deal of stress is generated by a sense of guilt that we've violated that code, or perhaps just the knowledge that at some level we've done wrong.

Sometimes our stress comes from an awareness that we've violated what we consider to be "God's laws." We've lied, stolen, cheated on a spouse. All our attempts at rationalizing haven't helped. Down deep we feel terrible. At other times, our stress comes from the awareness we've violated our own "code."

And when we do, it's as if there's a flashing red light inside telling us we've done something that violates the sense that living consistent with a "code of conduct" is foundational to our spiritual and relational health.

Claire was vaguely aware that the uncomfortable feeling she got when she padded her expense account report was more than worry about losing her job if she got caught. She had tried to justify her actions for a long time, but when she finally was honest with herself, she realized that the uncomfortable feeling came from a belief that taking something you have not gotten by honest means is wrong. It's no coincidence that tension headaches she'd been experiencing ceased when she decided it was time to live more honestly.

Some of us respond to that flashing light by ignoring it, as Claire tried to for a time. We would like to just put a piece of duct tape over it and pretend it's not flashing. Or we focus outward and insist that everyone else's red light is flashing, too. This is a diversionary tactic. And though we can almost trick our heads into believing our violation is "not that big a deal," our conscience knows the truth. To act this way—not taking responsibility for wrongs—is simply to bury stress and give it malignant power. It sets us up for possible emotional and even physical illness.

Only when we accept responsibility do we turn things around. Admitting our wrong is our big chance to get back on the track of wellness in spirit and body. To continue hiding our failure is to bury deep inside us the negative energy that guilt-stress creates. It is to promote sickness, first in spirit and then in body. To accept responsibility is to end the stress that exists between what we're doing and the code we believe in. It gives us the strength to change our wrongdoing into right-doing. And at the same time, it puts us back on the path of balance and well-being.

The first step (and the hardest) is to face up to the truth. Few of us actually like to face the truth about ourselves. It just doesn't come naturally. What does come naturally is to dodge the truth, block it from our minds. When pushed, we blame and rationalize our actions.

For this reason, it's a great idea to have someone present to listen when we finally decide to clear the inner atmosphere. This spiritual discipline of confession needs to be done in the presence of a member of the clergy, or that of a counselor or trusted friend.

Why? Because oddly enough, something good happens when we face another flesh-and-blood person and admit the worst about ourselves. We can kid ourselves into thinking even a huge violation is "just a momentary slip," when in fact it is evidence of some great need we're trying to meet in a wrong way.

Speaking the truth about ourselves to another is healthy. It helps bring our true self out into the open where we can deal with it. It also helps to bring closure to events which, because they've been hidden, have been incomplete. And so they continue to have power to affect our lives. In that sense, confession is a capstone, "capping off" the flow of guilt, shame, and remorse... allowing us to move on.

Confession can also help in another way.

Some of us are the overresponsible types. We spend too much time hip-wading around in the murky lower depths of our soul. We seem bent on finding something wrong in our words and actions. We are plagued by what the old saints called "a scrupulous conscience." This is as much a plague to the spirit as refusing to take responsibility for violating spiritual laws or the code we live by.

Our problem is that we are overfocused on ourselves. We may believe that our actions are "buying" us something from God, like special favors or blessings, or keeping us free from divine punishment. Underneath it all we are driven by an unhealthy fear of God— not the enthusiasm that comes from holding a positive, healthy belief in God.

Confession, for some, will turn into an event in which our trusted "confessor" says, "Lighten up. You're too hard on yourself. Shift your focus to what you're doing *right.*"

Strategy 4: Revisit Our Thinking About God

At some point, it's necessary to revisit what we believe about God. We touched on this earlier in discussing core beliefs.

We may believe, for instance, that God is only accepting of "good" or "perfect" or "saintly" people—people whose records are filled with charitable acts. Or we may think God only showers "blessings" on the happy, nice-looking, competent people because they seem to have everything going for them. At the same time we may think God is angry at us or coldly indifferent to our struggles, or that we've been unfairly overlooked in the "blessing" department.

Often our picture of God is one we got from a parent or religious figure. If they displayed attitudes of superiority, disgust, disdain, or loathing toward us, we might think that's how God is. We think their too-high standards are God's standards. We think their way of punishing us for not being good enough has divine approval. Or we mistake our parents' lack of care for cosmic neglect. We think, "If Mom and Dad didn't like me, God must not like me."

Such a misunderstanding of the nature of God can only intensify the problems that stress us. It's when we know that God accepts us—even when other people may not—that we're empowered to walk through adversity with confidence.

It may be helpful to remember that an older wisdom tells us God has many "faces"—or aspects. One of these faces can be described as nurturing, kind, merciful, and forgiving. Once we are honest with ourselves, we need to be aware of what we're doing when we remain unforgiving toward our failures. We need to recognize that the harsh face of judgment staring at us so wrathfully may, in fact, be the one we see in the mirror. And we need to look beyond our self-condemnation to see the Face that looks at us with forgiveness.

As one biblical writer puts it, "If God be for us, who can be against us?"[9] The answer is, sometimes we can be our own worst enemy. We continue to accuse ourselves long after God has forgiven us. Perhaps we feel that if we "beat ourselves up enough," God will decide to go light on us because we've done the job already.

Why don't we accept the truth? We can accept the forgiveness God offers. We can also experience inner freedom from the stresses that crush us in spirit if we would honestly face the problem that's stressing us.

Our spiritual task is to make the step toward peace that comes when we actually do believe we are forgiven.

This task also must include discarding our old, negative, one-sided images of God that have kept us from a true relationship. Taking on this task is a freeing exercise that helps us take an important step toward spiritual well-being.

One image of God you may need to consider, perhaps for the first time, is the image of a God who loved us all enough to come down from heaven...to be one of us...to teach and guide us...and to stretch out his arms on a cross...and there to take all our blame upon himself so we can be free. Accepting God's complete forgiveness and welcome is a great beginning to a new and healthful relationship.

Strategy 5: Develop a Real Relationship with God

Although a relationship with God is an important strategy in reducing stress, it's not a "quick fix." Even people of faith can suffer from stress and its effects. Even people of faith can have wrong attitudes about God.

Our relationship to God can also suffer when we fail to do the frequent, honest, and soul-searching work that promotes robust spiritual health.

At the most basic level, we all need a constant supply of spiritual wisdom—truth that is broader and deeper than "logic" to help us cope with life. Wisdom helps us integrate the unexplainable into our lives.

Where do we begin then?

Perhaps we have been stuck on a question of injustice. A good place to begin is to open ourselves to the possibility that we are missing a spiritual perspective that would help make sense of a painful event. Then we can ask for insight from beyond our own perspective. When we do so, we open ourselves more to that little "light of insight" that comes on inside. And we deepen our connection with God.

Maybe we feel we've been abandoned and left on our own, when help would have kept us from struggling and suffering. Then we need to begin by being open to recognizing the times when help *was* there for us, and acknowledging the character qualities that could have grown in us by no other means than by lonely struggle.

When we start to see all we've gained, not only what we have lost, through our effort we may begin to wonder, "Is it possible that a wiser being was involved in guiding our "life education" and character growth after all?"

Or perhaps we've been neglecting our spiritual side because of a serious "violation of code." Then we can begin by asking that our eyes be open to the grace that seems fairly rampant in the universe. It is by this grace that all of us are daily, hourly, offered a new beginning.

Strategy 6: Make Amends Where Possible

Many stress-relief strategies involve learning how to avoid tension. Sometimes, however, it takes *facing* tension in order to release it. This is true when it comes to wrongs we've done to other people.

We will never let go of spiritual stresses we've reaped from hurting someone until we make amends. The hurtful things we've done are like muscle knots in our relationships, and they have to be worked out.

When we need to make amends for a harm we've caused—for what we've done, or what we've failed to do—nothing works as well as the advice given in Nike's famous ad campaign: Just do it. You'll be amazed at the sense of balance and peace that comes when you've made that apology or attempted to right that wrong.

The responsibility to deal with stressors may be ours alone, but we don't have to BE alone.

Strategy 7: Involve Yourself in a Community of Spiritual People

Companies that sell life and health insurance have made many millions of dollars targeting their sales to religious people. Why? Because people who are part of a spiritual community—a fellowship of people who support their values and support *them*—not only tend to have healthier physical habits, but they also seem to have more efficient ways of dealing with inner tensions that nuke those without this resource.

Spiritual communities can offer us a place to explore our connection to God. They also provide emotional and practical support, a safe place to be confidential and to unburden our souls, and a source of steadying friendships.

To have pressure and difficulty is part of being human. True, the responsibility to deal with stressors may be ours alone, but we don't have to *be* alone while we do so. We can reach out for support while we do what we have to do.

You don't have to sign up for lifetime membership or promise away your firstborn to become part of a spiritual community and enjoy the benefits of finding friends with whom you know you belong. Consider adding this to your cache of spiritual health strategies.

Spiritual "Tonics"

A moment ago, I mentioned that a healthy relationship with God requires frequent, honest, and soul-searching work. We can't simply go through the motions in any relationship and expect to gain. It's only in the context of relationship to God, to others, and to ourselves that any "techniques" make sense.

That said, here are some techniques that act like tonics for the spirit.

Strategy 8: "Connected" Praying

Sometimes even spiritual people experience "dryness" or boredom in prayer. Others often have a hard time just getting started. Usually this is because the form of prayer we're using has no benefit, or our prayers seem repetitive, maybe even boring.

Often the things we think we *ought* to pray about have no connection with what we're experiencing in our own spirit. If you are already a praying person, with a list of heartfelt requests for God, you don't have to set aside that kind of prayer to benefit from another type.

"Connected praying" is a simple technique that's much like stream-of-consciousness writing. It's a wonderful balm for relieving inner stress.

To begin, you only need to let go of formality and dive into the flow—the stream-of-consciousness—of your own thoughts. Allow your running thoughts and feelings to continue, but imagine them as a current flowing out in a stream that's open to God.

Be aware when you start to "overthink" or "correct" yourself: "I know I shouldn't feel this way" and "I really didn't mean that, God," have no place here.

The trick is not to censor anything, whether fantasies or daydreams, aspirations or losses. Let all that's in you—happiness, sorrow, questions, depression, boredom, irritation, wonder, or the small joys of living—just *be*.

The point of connected praying is to move closer to our own "ground of being"—that deep place inside where the real us stands more fully honest, more open before God. It is to be honest about the many parts of ourselves we conceal—imagining we can hide them even from God. God welcomes us to do so. It's in this complete openness that we know and are known.

To the believing person, the benefit of connected praying is that we become more honest about who we are, in our strengths and passions, and in our weaknesses. We also open ourselves to the guidance and "course corrections" God has for us. The more honest and open we are, the clearer we "hear" God speaking within us.

Through connected praying we learn to quickly let go of the past. For some reason, we tend to rehash the negative and the failures in our past, rather than dwelling on the positive and the growth we've achieved. This negative rehashing creates inner stress as we relive events, mistakes, and losses that cannot be recalled or redone.

Big unresolved issues and questions are likely to come up. If so, gently set them aside to be dealt with at another time. For now, turn yourself back into the current of the moment and continue. Don't worry if your thoughts wander from one thing to another: a concern about a friend...the roof needing repair... some jerk at work who knifed you in the back.

Eventually, you'll find that your spirit is being energized by one or more dominant emotions. Often they're negative emotions: fear, anger, sadness, anxiety. *Bingo.* From a health standpoint, the benefit of this kind of praying is that when we relax we tend to let out what's been eating us from within. This is the time to let it all the way out, to let it go by leaving it to God's care.

Many people will attest that, once they prayed this way—"clearing out all the clutter," getting in touch with their real feelings about a matter, inviting God into the picture—direction came.

When we pray this way, we become more connected to our selves and to our Maker, because we are simply "moving with God" in the present moment. Some people practice this sort of "God awareness" until it's a subtle part of their daily routine. As a final benefit, they discover that even their most ordinary day is full of life's simple goodnesses, and that they're better off than they thought.

Strategy 9: Sacred and Inspirational Reading

In exploring sacred and inspirational writings, there is great "tonic" for the soul. With all the struggle and stress life tosses at us, we need the spiritual direction and wise perspectives such writings offer.

When we open ourselves to time-honored scriptures and spiritual writings we connect our spirit to a breadth of human experience and spiritual wisdom that offers us inner balance. The same can be true when we read the works of poets and essayists whose insights and spiritual experiences inspire us with hope, peace, and broader perspectives about living.

Many people make sacred and inspirational reading their habit, either at the opening of the day or at night before bed. Others tuck a small book of readings in their purse or briefcase to refresh them during breaks at work.

Just a few of the stress-relieving benefits of sacred and inspirational reading are:

- *Centering.* Wisdom is insight that helps us to make sense of life and its mysteries, complexities, and absurdities. We need wisdom to center us and to remind us of what's essential when life's tensions and unanswered questions are pulling us apart.

- *Comfort of shared experience.* Many of the ancient spiritual writers bared their souls in ways modern writers do not. In them we find our own stresses, depressions, complaints, longings, and hopes mirrored back to us. And we understand ourselves and our reactions better.

- *Perspective.* In sacred and inspirational writings we find the long view of life. We discover deeper meaning in life's events—in our passages, losses, successes, and joys. We learn to relax, and we better understand all that we share in common—the good and the bad—with every other human being.

> ## "In the depths of winter, I finally learned that within me lay an invincible summer."
> —ALBERT CAMUS

"Tonic" for the Spirit

To get the most "tonic" effects from your spiritual reading, choose literature that:

- *Strengthens your convictions.* In spirit, as in body, we have a naturally lazy streak. We would like to live on "soul candy" that tastes good going down but which offers no lasting benefit. Beware of writing that is just "comfort food." It will make you flabby. Conviction is soul muscle. Conviction is what causes us to take part in purposes that lie beyond our immediate self-centered interests. The best spiritual literature encourages us to believe...and to *act.*

- *Challenges you to examine your moral stance.* The human spirit innately knows there is a "right" and "wrong." We also know there are universal standards. Avoid writings that suggest what's right and wrong is solely up to you. Alcoholics Anonymous has known for decades that "taking a searching moral inventory" is a step that does wonders for every one of us. We need the astringent quality of writings that correct us.

- *Offers new glimpses of God.* We are very often shortsighted, even blind, when it comes to understanding God. In the words of the psalmist, God is "manifold"—full of wonders and graces we just don't see. Spiritually "tonic" writing opens the eyes of the inner man, so we say, "I never saw God *that* way before."

Sacred and inspirational writings are a doorway from the limited now to the infinite. We learn to trust that, though we can't always produce hard proof of it, God is at work on our behalf.

Soul Food

My own spiritual tradition is broadly Christian, and gives me a taste for spiritual reading that likes to dine abroad. Some favorites are as follows. You can make a good meal from these writings, as have many discriminating readers.

Appetizers (*to make you glad you came*)

Pilgrim at Tinker Creek (Annie Dillard, HarperCollins)

Candles in the Dark (and anything else by Amy Carmichael, Christian Literature Crusade)

Entrées (*classic richness!*)

Contemplative Prayer (Thomas Merton, Doubleday/Image)

The Confessions (both St. Augustine's and St. Patrick's)

The Christian's Secret of a Happy Life (Hannah Whitall Smith, Revell)

Revelations of Divine Love (Julian of Norwich)

Dark Night of the Soul (St. John of the Cross—It's not what you're expecting!)

The Knowledge of the Holy (A. W. Tozer, HarperCollins)

The Divine Conspiracy (Dallas Willard, HarperCollins)

The Bible—especially the Psalms, Proverbs, and the wisdom books of Job, Ecclesiastes, and the apocryphal book of Sirach.

Light Contemporary Fare (*good and satisfying!*)

The Road Less Traveled (M. Scott Peck)

The Return of the Prodigal Son (Henri Nouwen, Doubleday/Image)

Telling Yourself the Truth (William Backus, Bethany House Publishers)

The Chronicles of Narnia (C. S. Lewis)

Strategy 10: Solitude and Silence

Solitude and silence are ancient spiritual practices that go hand in hand, and their tremendous contributions to well-being are now being rediscovered.

Solitude is essentially the practice of getting alone and away from it all. No cell phones. No take-along work. You can start with just a day or a weekend and build up to a full week if you find this practice suits you and your schedule. A park, a campground, or a retreat center all work well. If you can't get away, a favorite over-stuffed chair in a quiet room will do. The point is to get away from the demands that give us that stressed, scattered feeling.

Silence gives us the chance to practice a kind of prayer known to spiritually resilient people throughout the ages. Contemplative prayer is somewhat misnamed, in that it doesn't involve the use of words at all. In fact, it's exactly the opposite of "connected prayer" with its streaming thought-line.

The goal of silent or contemplative prayer is to bring your mind, emotions, and spirit to complete stillness, to experience a profound state of rest. This deep, inner rest is wonderful, spreading through your entire being. Very refreshing!

Let's be clear. In order to practice this kind of inner silence, it's not necessary to imagine yourself opening up to some "spiritual source of energy" or to "deep truth from the cosmos." You are not opening your soul so you can be a "channel" for some other "entity" claiming to be from a faraway galaxy. The goal is just to achieve a deeply satisfying, state of quiet. Expect that it will take practice to achieve even a few moments of contemplative stillness. Here are some practical steps to guide you:

- *Get alone* in a place where you won't be disturbed.

- *Get comfortable.* Sitting in a comfortable chair, with legs and arms relaxed is preferable. Keep your head upright. You want to maintain a state of awareness (not fall asleep!).

- *Get focused.* Breathe in slowly through your nose. Relax and breathe out. Direct your attention to the tide of this gentle, natural rhythm.

- **Get ready.** After a time, you will experience calming silence. For some, a deep sense of relaxation moves throughout their whole being, like the gentle circle of a ripple that spreads from a pebble dropped in water. At the same time, you find yourself remarkably alert to the quiet and stillness and to any insight or direction that comes.

Among other things, silent prayer is likely to help us uncover some of those hidden core beliefs that have been pumping frustration into our lives. We definitely find ourselves nourished and recharged from the center of our being. Instead of stressful energy shooting haywire in every direction, fatiguing us, we're focused and positively energized.

Strategy 11: Responding from the Stable Stance of Inner Peace

Spiritual benefits aside, there is a very practical end-goal to the stress-relief strategies in this chapter. It's to help us change the stressed-out way we respond to life's tensions.

In an earlier chapter, we talked about becoming "stress batteries," storing up charges of insecurity and fear, sadness, or frustration and anger. All it takes is for a small button to be pushed and stress zings through our whole system. Worse, we zap other people and make ourselves more miserable with stressed-out reactions... often to little things. (If you've ever shouted at a small child for spilling milk or pounded your fists on the steering wheel at a red light, you know what I mean.)

Learning how to change our reactions to life's relatively small stressors will give us good practice for those truly big challenges that inevitably come our way. Rather than reacting from an off-balance stance of stress, we can learn how to respond from a stable stance of peace.

It may help to picture our response to a stressful event or person this way:

Let's slow down something that happens at the speed of electricity charging through wires.

Stressor

Response Under Pressure

The stressor. The arrow on the left represents an incident that brings stress, be it a piece of unwelcome news, an insult or slight, or a grating or whiny voice demanding our attention when we're frazzled. Let's say we're in a sales meeting, and someone points out a mistake in our presentation, or who simply acts rude.

Our interpretation. Normally speaking, we interpret a stressor as an "invader." It is something that's come to wreck our peace, quiet, and contentment—the "all is well" sense we like to have. Deep down, we're disturbed. Fear (or more likely, irritation) builds. We tell ourselves, "I'm such a dope. I blew it." Or "I hate this guy. I'd like to…"

The reaction. Then comes the flash of loud, terrified, complaining, or angry words. Maybe a retreating reaction like tears, pouting, or despondency…or aggressiveness, threats, and blaming. In reaction, we may give a sarcastic reply. (Or experience "flop sweat" and freeze.) Or "act the professional" and press on, while our presentation gets more mechanical and dead by the second.

The problem is, stress rules the moment. A stressed-out reaction almost never helps us, and it usually makes things worse. What we can do is to practice adding another step, which allows calm to come in. Consider the picture on the next page.

The *stressor* is identical. What's different is that we've added a *pause.* Many of us do not give ourselves the benefit of a small break when we're under stress.

We can try the following the next time someone takes delight in nuking our presentation. If possible, we can excuse ourselves or ask to go get a glass of water or for a moment to answer the call of nature. If nothing else, we can say, "Give me just a moment to think about that." Anything to halt the stress-reaction cycle.

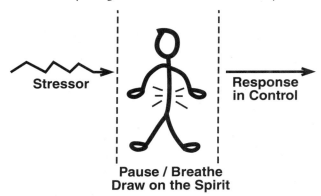

Stressor

Response in Control

Pause / Breathe
Draw on the Spirit

During the momentary pause, we can revisit our own core. We don't need to react to the negative thrust of the stressor. We can respond evenly out of who we are and what we believe and value. Taking a momentary break from the sales meeting, we take a deep breath, regain perspective, and remind ourselves that *calm* and *respect* are our core values.

When we return, not surprisingly, calm and a respectful tone rule the moment. And whatever the ultimate outcome, we've gained some ground in our own soul. That alone is worth it all.

Obviously, this final strategy is most beneficial when you've added other spiritual strategies—prayer, sacred reading, solitude, and silent contemplation—to your regimen of well-being practices. That's because these strategies change the quality and character of your spirit.

When you allow your spirit to draw from a deeper well—from sources of help and peace beyond you—you will experience vitality, inner strength, balance, and calm. It cannot be otherwise because you have opened and cleared the connection to God Himself.

Then, no matter what outward circumstances throw at you, you will be better equipped to live from a center of peace and stability, rather than becoming a stressed-out victim of life on this planet.

Why not begin to create a simple regimen of spiritual practices today? You will begin to experience the strength and personal growth you want. *Trust it.*

Got Salvation?

~

Experiencing "salvation" includes the concept of healing or "salving" the whole person. Since God created us body, mind, and soul, it only makes sense that a healthy relationship with our Creator should balance and bring well-being to our whole person.

Which of the strategies and techniques in this chapter do you need to help bring "healing salve" to your inner being? Which ones will begin to relieve the spiritual tension that's compromising your total well-being?

(4)
All That Work You Do

Are you carrying too heavy a load of work—on the job, at home, or in a relationship? Is it stressing you out?

Good news! You are not a camel. That hump between your shoulders is a head. It doesn't hold fat and water; it contains a brain. That being so, please think about this: Human beings were made to do more than *work, work, work.* And one person probably cannot do all that *you* are trying to do.

But It's My Job...

Face it: You hate it. Some aspect of your job, or maybe the work itself, is tiresome to you. Day after day you find it a drain on your emotions, your creativity, and your physical being. Dutiful person that you are, provider that you are, you've stayed at it. Not only are you maxed out at work, your responsibilities at home may be stretching you even thinner—and multiplying your stress.

Some of us are responsible for a list of tasks at home that would break a draft horse. For most women, the title "Chief Cook and Bottle Washer" doesn't even begin to tell the weight of jobs and chores that rest on their shoulders. Men, too, come home to find jobs around the house that must be done: yard work, minor repairs, bills to pay. And both men and women with children have the additional responsibilities that being a good parent entails.

Others of us bear the stress of overwork because we're in relationships that overload us. Sometimes we're put in a position where we have to give and give, or we put ourselves in that position. If we were trained at a young age to be an emotional beast of burden, working too hard in a given relationship may even seem normal.

And then some of us are virtual dynamos in every arena. We're not type A; we're at least double A. We outperform others at work, at home, and maybe in the job of emotional burden-bearing, too. But *virtual dynamo* is the operative term. In reality we're not superheroes imbued with unnatural strength and endurance. Yes, we can probably keep up the pace, but all the while we're depleting our spirit and heading for physical and emotional exhaustion.

News Flash: *It is not our responsibility to do the hard job or the whole job all the time.*

At Work

Is your job stressing you out? Is your attitude toward your work eating away at you?

It's time to look honestly at some reasons why work, or your approach to it, may be compromising your well-being. What follows is a self-test. How many of these stress-inducing situations are you experiencing? Check each one that applies:

____ ***Too many tasks.*** Multitasking is one of those big buzzwords these days. Whether you're a tapped-out executive or an at-home mom who's homeschooling, cleaning, cooking, and scheduling your family's life, you're called on to perform three, four, or five tasks all at once and most of the time.

____ ***Too little time.*** Everything needs to be done today. Yesterday would have been better. Why isn't it done now? Deadlines are aptly named because by the time you reach the line, you're all but…well, you get it.

____ ***Too much competition.*** The message you get is, "If you can't handle this job, there are 3.2 million other people waiting to take your place." Or you live with the anxiety that others are pulling ahead and you've got to work longer, harder…or be cut out.

____ ***People cheat.*** You have coworkers who'll take over your ideas or your clients if you aren't on guard every minute.

____*Goals are too high.* You or your employer have set quotas and goals that are way over your head.

____*Too few breaks, or no breaks.* You eat at your desk. A "break" is a much-needed trip to the restroom.

____*Low morale.* Something weighs down the atmosphere, and people are generally dissatisfied.

____*A threatening atmosphere.* You're in physical danger. You're being sexually harassed or verbally abused.

____*Not qualified.* Somehow you landed in a job for which you're not trained. You're in over your head and you know it.

____*No room for growth.* You thought there was more potential in this job. Or you've discovered you have more value and potential than you thought. But there's nowhere to go here. You're going to be stuck in the same role with the same pay.

____*You feel there's no way out.* There are a million reasons why people feel trapped in their work. Of course, it's not true that you're trapped. But if you feel this way, for the record, what's your reason?

____*Others are working against you or aren't pulling their weight.* You're part of a machine that's grinding against itself. The work of another person, or a department makes your job much tougher.

____*Poor management.* There's no vision, no leadership, no skill in the levels above you. Or there's a willingness to sacrifice underlings for higher profits or to cover mistakes. Or no one listens to those who actually do the jobs, the ones who know how the work should be done.

____*No passion for it.* As you drive home every day, you ask yourself, "Is this how I'm going to spend my life?" You wanted to do X with your life, but are doing Y. And there's a real ache in your soul for something else.

The Opposite of Work

When our work is a major source of stress, we need to rebalance our life. We need something at the opposite end to level us out again.

What's the opposite of work? Some of us would say "sleep" or "a long vacation." That's because we think the opposite of work is just something that gives us a break from it.

But if your work is the major cause of the stress in your life, the answer is something other than these things. The opposite of that kind of work is *enjoyment.*

You may be thinking, "Get real."

Before you brush this off, consider:

- Do you live in order to work, or do you work in order to support yourself while you enjoy things that make life worth living? When was the last time you enjoyed them?

- What *is* your life? Where do you find meaning, purpose?

- What makes you feel glad to be alive? What do you enjoy? To help you clarify further, take another minute to finish this sentence honestly:

I work in order to_____.

Rating Some Answers

Many, many answers are possible. But if you answered:

- *"...fulfill my duty,"* rate your attitude *joyless.* Your stress comes from a life that's too narrow-focused and without variety or color.

- *"...get a paycheck,"* rate your attitude *stale.* Your stress comes from dissatisfaction, and boredom will soon show up if it hasn't already in your work and in your attitude toward the rest of life.

- *"...beat out my competitor(s),"* *"to show other people what I can do,"* or *"to show what I'm really worth,"* rate your attitude that of a *slave.* Other people and their opinions have great power over you. Your stress comes from working to conquer an invisible opponent that you'll never beat.

- *"...get the bucks for a car, bigger house, boat, second home, great vacations, etc,"* rate your attitude *insatiable.* Your stress comes from the fact that, like the wild predator, your satisfaction lasts only as long as the "hunt." When you've bagged the latest item on your wish list, you grow tired of it and need to live and work for something else.

- *"...support someone else who's reaching for their dream,"* rate your attitude **admirable**...for now. Also rate yourself **potential miserable martyr** if you don't know when to draw the line and begin working for your own goals and your own enjoyment of life.

- *"...make as much as I can now so I can retire early,"* rate yourself high in the ability to delay gratification, but rate your attitude that of a **gambler.** Your stress comes from being unable to enter into the life you have right now. You may be missing your children's irretrievable growing-up years, along with the many simple joys that life sets before us every day, betting the gold that's in your hands right now on a future that's guaranteed to no one.

Strategy 1: Do What You Love

As discussed earlier, one of the main strategies for relieving stress and promoting total well-being is to replace unhealthy core beliefs and attitudes that unbalance us. In relation to work, probably the most healthy core belief we can live by is this: *I was made to do what I love.*

Wisdom of the ages has it that each of us came into this world with a "spark of life." This fire is the passion, of our soul—our likes, desires, and inborn gifts and skills.[10] If we're doing work that takes us away from our natural passions, we're following a path that's not ours to walk. Our "fire" dwindles. We struggle and strain with our work because it's just not "us."

Relieving work-related stress may require other strategies as well, but it surely starts at this core level. It begins by adopting the attitude: "I need to do what I love to do. Insofar as work goes, I'll do better at my job...and I'll be happier and more balanced."

Ask people who truly love what they do. Work seems lighter, obstacles are mere speed bumps. A general sense that "all's right with the world" accompanies them through the day.

Strategy 2: Change Focus

Maybe you *are* doing what you love, just too much of it under pressure, or for too long. In chapter 2, we saw much how it helps to change from an intense, convergent focus to a relaxed divergent one.

You might think that taking breaks and inserting moments of blue-sky thinking into your day would distract you. But your mind can work like a muscle. We need to break up periods of intense work with periods of relaxation. We can't always "go for the burn" and expect to not burn out.

If location allows, you may want to step outside and/or away from your work environment to take your relaxed-focus break and add in a short walk. Getting your metabolism moving when you've been sitting all day is another stress reliever.

Strategy 3: Get a Life...Your Life

Complete this sentence:
I work in order to enjoy_____.

The more we think that working to support the enjoyment of life sounds "unrealistic," the more we probably need to do so. Some of us entered the working world with future dreams in mind. But along the way, we overlearned the lessons about delayed gratification. Like a seedling lying pale and dormant under a stone slab, what we once dreamed lies within us still, yearning to push off the crushing weight so we can really live our dreams before it's too late.

Perhaps the thing that would bring back the joy of living is as simple as spending more time in nature, or taking the music lessons you always wanted, or taking up a sport you've always loved. The simpler and less expensive, the better.

Continue to fight it or scoff if you want to, but *why* when the life of your soul is on the line?

Strategy 4: Off-load

If your stress comes from too much work or multitasking or too many deadline pressures, you need to off-load. *Fast.*

Maybe you started by believing you were Superboy or Wondergirl. Now it's time to admit you're not. Or maybe you felt pressed into saying yes when you should have said no. Swallow your pride and say no now.

If you're in a position to reassign work, begin today to assess who's best able to handle some of your tasks. If you need to, make a careful written appeal to your boss. Don't hesitate to mention health concerns, out of fear of being replaced at your job. Most definitely list ways you'll be doing your job better overall once you have fewer tasks to do.

The other possibility with us type A personalities is that we take on too much because no one can do things up to our standard. But here's the truth: It's time to ease up on ourselves and everyone else in our world. *Our* stress has become *everyone else's* stress. We need to learn to give other people space to grow and to bring their own creativity and talents to the game.

> *"First, say to yourself what you would be.*
> *Then, do what you must do."*
> — EPICTETUS

Strategy 5: Make a Change

If you're in a job that isn't what you love, or if you've lost sight of what you first loved about your work, or if your appeals fall on deaf ears, have the intestinal fortitude to make a change.

Having said that, I admit that change isn't easy for any of us. Especially if we have more than just ourselves to support. When we're single, life can turn like a powerboat, on a dime. When we've got a family on board, it's more like trying to turn a barge.

Nonetheless, we need not stay stuck in a job that's stressing us out or isn't what we really want to do. We can take these steps:

1. Take a re-creation break. Take a whole day or a weekend and ask, "What is it I really like to do? If I could re-create my life, what would I be?" This is not the time to censor any of your answers. And you don't have to panic if it's not what you're doing right now. Let silence and solitude do their re-creating work in you.

2. Give ourselves permission to be "reinvented." Madonna's done it. Politicians and actors do it. We can "reinvent" ourselves and get onto the career path that's right for us. It may be as simple as switching departments in the same company or as involved as getting some new training so we can switch careers. But since we came into this world with a passion or a dream, the truth is we'll only find balance in our life by honoring that dream as the sacred gift it is.

It's important to let our dreams live for awhile just the way they are, to let ourselves daydream for some time. Then we may need to take another short break, perhaps another whole day to...

3. Give ourselves latitude in goal-setting. Now is the time for a bit of realism to set in. Every field has a range of jobs that might suit us. There are legal secretaries, and then there are supreme court judges. There are EMTs and brain surgeons. Given the whole range of our abilities and gifts, which role can we best fill in a given field?

4. Create a plan. Yes, it may require a long-term strategy. But it's important to our well-being that we do plan, and it's even more important that we work our plan. Does it involve requesting a certain college catalog? Writing your resumé?

Here's a tip to use in planning: Don't set deadlines—set goal lines. It feels great to cross one of those, to score a point for your passion and to say, "I did it!" One way of advancing toward your goal line is to budget time for incremental movement ahead. For instance, take a class or two that will move your plan forward. Or start that small business you've been dreaming of on-line. By starting to move ahead, however slowly, you'll lessen the stress of having to stay put for a while longer.

5. Give it time. Sometimes the very job we're looking for drops in our lap. Most of the time, it takes our effort...and time. Some of us don't get where we really want to go for no other reason than we can't endure our own impatience and frustration. We want to give up because our goal seems too far off.

℞

THE ART OF MAKING AN APPEAL

∽

We can make a diplomatic appeal to the person with the power to change things. A good appeal includes:

- *A clear statement of the work problem.* Briefly tell how the work is being affected. "I haven't been able to finish X in the time given because it consistently takes longer." *Also make sure you sound like you know what you're talking about.* "I've tracked this for a month, and it really does take that much time." Obviously, if abuse or harassment is the issue, that *is* the problem. Whoever is at fault should be faced in the presence of a superior.

- *Suggest a solution…don't insist on it.* Offering a creative solution can be helpful, as long as you don't push. "I've given this a lot of thought, and I have some ideas. Would you mind if I brought them up now?"

- *If a personal matter is involved, state that second.* Too often, we wait until we're under pressure, then we burst out with something like, "I never get out of here on time. They're always demanding too much of me. This place stinks." After you've shown concern and thoughtfulness about the work is the time to mention serious personal problems. "I've also been experiencing some pretty severe tension headaches, and so I really hope we can find a way to make a change."

- *Clarify and explain. Never argue.* Sometimes other people don't understand us the first time. If this seems to be the case, don't get an attitude. Ask if you can explain the problem one more time. You may have left something out.

- *Say thank you.* Whether a decision is made in your favor or not, nothing keeps the door open to your superior's office like politeness and respect. Maintain it at all times.

Making an appeal is an art, and one that's well worth learning.

The solution to this is to set several shorter goal lines on the way to our big goal, and to be realistic about how long the whole process can take. One secret to reinventing yourself vocationally is simply staying at it.

If we take even one step toward new work that we love, we'll see how deeply satisfying it is to be moving toward our passion… instead of staying stuck where we are.

Overwork in Relationships

Often, having to work too hard in relationships is a source of stress. Family and friends need us for support and help, but when the demand is too great, life becomes unbalanced and we suffer. We can also find ourselves in negative relationships—those in which we suffer from someone else's misuse or abuse. If we don't know how to change these relationships, we remain under mental, physical, emotional, or spiritual pressure. Stress endangers our well-being.

Here are some patterns that leave us straining under the load of unbalanced relationships:

Carrying needs. When people are truly incapable, or going through a particularly rough spot, they need us to help them shoulder the load. But the idea is to get them to a place down the road where they can begin to shoulder their own load again.

Some people refuse to carry their own load. They call month in and month out, always with the same problem. Nothing you suggest is the right solution. They want *you* to solve the problem. There may be something positive they're getting out of having the problem. (Attention and sympathy come to mind.) In either case, continuing to let your ear be the landfill for unsolvable problems is *not* helping. Eventually we feel irritable and tight when this person shows up.

Truly, it's better for all involved if you gently turn the problem back over to them. "If you could do anything at all to resolve this matter, what would it be?" is a good question to repeat. "Maybe we both need to take a break from this problem since nothing we can think of is helping" is a great boundary to set.

If we're the caring sort, this may be hard. Then we need to have faith in every person's ability to open up to a source of answers that's higher than we are.

Carrying responsibilities. Your spouse needs to make some calls, and you are pressed into making them. Your family should help with the care of an elderly relative, but you do it all. Your child has a school assignment, and you make the whole thing while your child hands you scissors, glue, and paint. Your family is bored, and you're supposed to be the director of fun. We become tense and exhausted much of the time. Maybe we feel used and angry, too.

Sometimes we let ourselves become too overloaded with the work other people should be doing. We overperform, allowing others to underperform. In no way is this teaching them how to work, or why it's important that they do their fair share. In fact, being a slave—even a willing one—is no favor at all. The rest of the world won't coddle them like we do. And a kick in the head with the frozen boot of reality lies just ahead.

Again, it's better for all involved if we gently turn back tasks to those who need to do them. If we're perfectionists and don't like the way our kids make their beds, we need to get over it. If we worry that our spouse won't pay the bills on time, we can endure our own worries for the sake of letting another adult step up to responsibility.

Keep in mind that if we've carried a job long enough, it may take a little while for the new sense of responsibility to kick in. Be patient, *and don't pick up the work again.*

Carrying emotions. A friend calls, depressed…and we are depressed. Our child is treated unfairly…and we seethe with righteous indignation for hours. Our spouse is offended…and we become an enemy to the offending party.

For some of us, it may be hard to detect in ourselves the stressful and damaging habit of carrying others' emotions. It's natural for us to pick up the emotional charge that belongs to other people and not realize we're doing it.

We need to learn that we are *not* other people. Letting our emotions become enmeshed with theirs does neither of us much good. Loving support and empathy, mixed with calm objectivity, is what our friends and family really need from us.

Carrying the whole relationship "investment." It takes two people, each one investing support, respect, encouragement, and practical help, to create a balanced relationship. Some of us are prone to carrying the whole investment. We buy ourselves flowers every time

℞

DIFFERENT KINDS OF ABUSIVE RELATIONSHIPS

∼

When we think of "abuse," we tend to think of hitting and angry, harmful words. Or we think of sexual abuse. If you're suffering from these kinds of abuse in silence, not recognizing the damage to you, *get help.*

Today make the call to a professional—whether your doctor, clergyman, or to a social agency—and take whatever steps you need to stop the attacks. *Don't stop seeking help until you get it.*

Sadly, there are other more subtle forms of abuse that we can live with for years, not recognizing the stress and destruction they cause. If you or someone you know is suffering from one of the following, *get help.*

Psychological abuse. Someone uses intimidating or degrading remarks, or their position of authority, to control you. Most especially, they have you convinced that you are too inept, or too weak to get by without them as dictator. You may experience this at work, in friendships, or at home.

Spiritual abuse. Someone uses their position as a representative of God to intimidate and control you. They have you convinced that you must do what they say or you will stand condemned before God. They may also have you convinced that you need them to be the "oracle of God" in your life.

"Crazy-making people." These are people who are constantly changing the terms, expectations, and demands in a relationship. They switch points in an argument in midstream. If their big deal was that you show up on time, they're upset and critical because you didn't wear the suit they thought you should wear. They ask you to do one favor, and are miffed that you didn't help them in some entirely different way. To let yourself be tyrannized by the constant changes of these people is to submit to the abuse of their illogic.

Abuse in all its forms is deeply disturbing to our whole psyche. Fear, anxiety, frustration, confusion, and lack of healthy self-will are indicators when abuse is present.

the other person forgets our special day and tell ourselves they were just too busy. We tell ourselves, "I know they like me. They just don't show it" to cover the deficit in their love and respect account with us.

This is called covering relational debts.

Difficult as it may be at first, we need to face the cold, hard balance sheet and admit it when we are the one carrying all the investment in a relationship.

Carrying the blame. Some people are *never* wrong. *You* are. Some people have to find a target for their frustration. You're it. Some people have to assign blame when there is no blame. Stuff happens, but you're handy, so they blame you.

Being the target of unfair blame is stress-inducing. It's also highly corrosive to a relationship. If you're unable to convince the blamer that you don't need to take unjust blame, put some space between you. Make it clear that you will not be a scapegoat.

If you overwork in relationships, a good rule to learn is: Don't do for others what they can be trained to do for themselves.

"But If I Don't Do It, It Won't Get Done"

Why do we allow ourselves to become stressed by overworking in relationships? There may be more complicated answers. But when all is said and done, we are most likely bothered by some variation of the same misgiving: "If I don't do this task, no one else will."

Usually, this simply is not the case. We don't see any help in sight—either because we've convinced ourselves that those right under our nose are *that* dependent, or because we haven't opened up our thinking to other sources of help.

Here are some steps you can take, if relationship stress is taxing your well-being:

Be ruthlessly honest with yourself. Is it true that others can't do the same job, or is it perfectionism? Is it true that things will fall apart in some way if you stop all your overworking? Maybe they should fall apart then. How else will a healthy new order of responsibilities be established.

Face our limitations. It's true: We can't be everything to the people we love. That doesn't mean we let them down intentionally. It just means we learn to live with an honest assessment of how much time, energy, know-how, wisdom, and patience we have. It means signaling when those commodities are tapped-out, or when they're needed for other things.

And when we state our limitations—"I'm sorry I can't help you right now"—it helps other people face our limitations, too. It also helps them to start thinking of how they can handle the matter in ways that don't draw from us.

→ ***Allow ourselves "breaks."*** We can stand up for ourselves and get a little rest to boot, when the demands seem endless. We can point out what we've contributed to the relationship in the past or take a "rain check" for the future. We can say, "I was able to do all those errands for you last week, but this week is a killer for me. Sorry." Or "I can do that job next time. Can you find someone else to help you this time?"

→ ***Learn to be a trainer.*** Sometimes our own competence is the problem. We think, "Oh, I'll just do it myself. It would be easier than trying to explain how it's done." In the short run, that's true. In the long run, we set ourselves up to be used again and again. Take the time to train. If you overwork in relationships, a good rule to learn is, Don't do for others what they can be trained to do for themselves. At least not on a long-term basis.

→ ***Live with it when every job isn't done right or isn't done at all.*** For some of us, this is the killer. We like closure. We like neatness. The problem is, we can't endure our own anxiety over an unfinished task long enough to let the truly responsible party experience the consequences of their inaction. In order to reestablish peace inside, we have to learn to let things go. And in order to let others step into their responsibilities, we have to live with the messy and the unfinished.

→ *"Staff for your weaknesses."* This is a great business maxim. Just as we have to learn the limits of our time and strength, we also have to learn the limits of our talent. Some of us are too self-assured, and some of us just don't want to say no, and others are too insecure to say, "I don't know how." To "staff for our weakness" means that we direct some of the work that's asked of us to other people who can do it better.

Caution: Don't Try This at Home

A final word about overwork in relationships.

Some of us are caught in a "give up/try harder cycle." We get burned out by the demands and so we give up. We say, "I'm through. I'm not doing this anymore. I'm exhausted." We may even actually take a break from whatever weight we've been carrying.

Time passes. We're a bit rested. The other person looks so helpless and fumbling. Maybe the other party still hasn't picked up on their responsibility. And after all, we know how to do it and we've done it before. Once again, we shoulder the load. We're apt to be thinking, "This time, if I try hard enough, they'll get the message, and they'll help." Welcome back to stress, fatigue, and resentment.

When we give up a task, we make a mistake if we use our "giving up" to manipulate the other person into taking action, or if we use giving up as a punishment ("Just see what happens *now*."). The only effective way out of this cycle is to truly give up and forfeit the responsibility to the one to whom it belongs. Period.

Keep this truth in mind: *Insanity is doing the same thing over and over...and expecting to get a different result.*

5

Stress and Your Diet

An old vaudeville joke goes, "There was a guy who went to bed feeling very anxious. In fact, he was so nervous that while he was sleeping he ate his own pillow."

"That's terrible. Did he get sick?"

"No. But he did wake up feeling a bit down in the mouth."

Okay. Hopefully you have the good sense not to use that one at parties. But it does illustrate the fact that there's a strong and complex connection between our emotions and our food intake.

Caution: Man-Eating Tiger

The truth is, life can be like a tiger that gnaws at us. And the stress of outer circumstances can dramatically affect our eating habits.

Conversely, what we consume can touch off biochemical reactions which stress our system and cause us to feel tense and unhealthy. Sometimes it's not what's eating us, but what we're eating that tips us off balance. Moreover, since what we eat affects so many hormonal interactions, even our regular eating habits if they're poor can tend to stress our whole system.

But before we look at any of these things, let's first consider what happens to our eating habits when circumstances begin to gnaw at us.

Mind Your Peas...

Saint Augustine said, "I approach food as I approach medicine."

At first glance this statement sounds rather...well...monkish and austere. Food as medicine? *Yippee.*

But there's actually a shrewd wisdom in his insight. It acknowledges that we do instinctively reach for food as a way to handle various needs, some physical and some emotional. The main reason for eating, lest we forget, is to nourish and build the body. Satisfying our palate, or getting a nice full feeling in the tummy, really is secondary. The point here is that we benefit if we develop the habit of mindful eating.

Mindful eating—as opposed to mindless eating—requires little mental energy. But it offers rich rewards by producing inner calm, better digestion, and a healthier diet. If you have ever crammed in a meal because you were pressured or in a hurry, you know how unsatisfying and unhealthy it can be to eat mindlessly under stress.

Mindful eating is more than just paying attention to what we put in our mouth, though it does include that. Could we stop right now and list what we ate today? Everything? Can we say if we enjoyed it? Was it healthy for us? Were we relaxed, or distracted, or tense while we ate? Learning to be aware of these things contributes to mindful eating.

Since it's much harder to digest food when we're under pressure and our body's energy is focused everywhere besides our digestive tract, mindful eating also makes mealtime a needed break from the world and its demands. To eat mindfully is to take the attitude that we need quiet and calm in which to eat. It is to purposely step out of the pressures of our day, to relax and enjoy the food we eat (not to mention the company we're in) in an unhurried, attentive way.

A good place to begin with mindful eating is to become aware of the way we eat *now,* especially when we're in the midst of stress.

"You know that what you eat you are."
—GEORGE HARRISON

℞

A MINDFUL MEAL

∿

Give time and thought this week to preparing a meal. It need not be gourmet, just healthy and balanced.

Give time and thought to a simple meat dish or pasta. If you can, visit a fruit and vegetable stand or market and pick out fresh produce. Sparkling cider or grape juice looks great even in cheap goblets. And a light dessert like fruit salad or low-fat ice cream adds a nice finishing touch.

Give time and thought to the table. An inexpensive bouquet or a clutch of wildflowers bring simple elegance.

Give time and thought to the person or people you'll be dining with. How have they *really* been? What are they thinking about? What's their wildest dream? What are they looking forward to? If your plan is to dine alone, take time to ponder these questions yourself.

What you're likely to notice is that it takes almost no effort to add the two most important ingredients in this experience: Time and thought. Add those two things to *anything*—be it the moments you spend planning to grocery shop, or an afternoon with a child, or an evening with your spouse or friend— and you are guaranteeing yourself a life seasoned with peaceful and bright-spirited times.

Are You a "Stuffer," a "Starver," or...?

Stress has an almost immediate effect on the way we eat. Unfortunately, most of us don't recognize when our normal eating habit changes. Things get tense, and we slip into stress eating mode.

There are several stress eating patterns. Which one do you fall into?

Cramming. Most of us would protest if someone accused us of "cramming" our food. Mother told us not to. But every day in hasty breakfasts, in "power" business lunches, and in dinners eaten on the fly we do indeed cram. Is there any surer sign that we, as a culture, do violence to ourselves and our lives with stress eating?

Stuffing. For some of us, tension triggers nervous energy that seems to center in our jaws. It's not that we're hungry; it's that we need a stick of gum. And when the whole pack is gone, we need a cookie. And when the whole box is gone…

Emotions like sadness, boredom, or anxiety can trigger stress eating. The same is true with pressured circumstances like a work deadline. Sometimes we graze. Oddly enough, some of us can do this and then look someone straight in the eye and say, "Gee, I really didn't eat a thing all day." Other people gorge and feel terrible afterward.

Starving. Under pressure, some of us grit our teeth and refuse to eat. The thought of food is mildly disgusting. Over the course of days, we may nibble here and there, but we never take in enough calories and nutrients needed to help ourselves through the rough spot. Joking about it, saying, "I'll just live off the fat of the land," doesn't begin to solve the real problem we're causing for ourselves.

"Comfort" bingeing. Let the tension hit, and off we go, consuming huge amounts of our favorite "comfort" food. It might be somewhat benign (though fattening) such as potato chips by the bag full, a half-gallon of ice cream, or chocolate bars in quantity. Or we may subject ourselves to the more damaging effects of something like alcohol consumption. (Then we straighten up and tell ourselves it won't happen again.)

Anorexia, bulimia, and body dysmorphia. Starving, gorging and purging, and seeing a distorted image of your body—these disorders are related to stress, and they are becoming more and more common today. Because they can have deep emotional and/or biochemical roots, it's outside the scope of this book to discuss them at length or offer help in detail. But it's important that you realize these disorders require outside help in order to overcome them.

Take note, however, that stress is often an immediate trigger for one of these disorders. Because they affect that hazy connection between the psyche and the body, they also affect our approach to food.

If you think you suffer from one of these disorders, contact a professional counselor and your medical doctor at once. Long-term psychological and physical effects can be turned around if you seek help immediately. Many people are finding relief and freedom from these disorders.

The immediate physical effects of stress eating patterns are severe blood-sugar peaks and dips and hormonal fluctuations. Depending on our pattern, we can either feel lethargic and groggy or jittery within minutes. Mentally, we become vague or so "wired" that we're unable to zero in on the matter at hand. Psychologically and emotionally, we're ingraining one of two habits: either to compensate ourselves or to over control when we're troubled.

The bottom line is that any form of stress eating throws our body off-kilter at a time when we most need it to be steady, strong, and in balance. What we need is to begin with a new eating habit all the time.

Decide now to eat for total well-being.

When you say no to one habit,
you also have to say yes to a
healthier new habit.

Strategy 1: Eating for Overall Well-being

The first thing we need is a plan to reverse stress eating. Here are some helpful steps:

1. *Take note of the people, situations, even places, that trigger stress eating.* It's the unexpected stress that springs the trap on us. Make mental notes, or if necessary keep a small pad handy to record your stress triggers. They may surprise you.

2. *Become aware of your stress eating type.* When you're stressed, what do you eat? Where? Are you a "grazer," sneaking constant snacks that "don't count"? Do you gorge? Or do you cut off your food supply?

3. *Look for connections that explain why you do what you do.* Take time to check your self-talk.

If you go into conveyor-belt eating mode, you may be telling yourself something like, "All this pressure makes me feel [X], so I deserve the good feeling eating [Y] gives me." Or "This stress is taking [X] away from me, so I deserve to eat something good to make up for the loss."

As already mentioned, in the case of eating disorders you will most benefit from seeking professional support as you look for any of these contributing connections.

4. *Eat for your overall well-being.* This begins with being honest with ourselves about both our intake habits *and* our diet. An eating plan that will promote overall wellness and reduce physical stress to our system will be made up of 50 to 75 percent raw foods like fruits, vegetables, and small amounts of grain. It will not include fried food, junk food, and sodas.

5. *Have an alternative plan and begin it.* When you plan to tell yourself no to one habit, you also have to be ready to tell yourself yes to a healthier new habit.

When it comes to eating, the best habit is to find a plan that helps you maintain a balanced metabolism throughout the day. We are not focusing on weight-loss here, though if you're carrying too much body fat and you change your eating habits, weight loss may also result.

Diets geared to helping you maintain stable insulin, hormonal, or energy levels generally help you to develop a stable eating habit. There is no better way to say no to stress eating patterns than to develop this new pattern, which means eating smaller, more frequent meals balanced with protein, carbohydrates, and minimal fat.

If stress catches you unaware, remember: The goal is to keep your blood sugar and hormonal levels near constant in order to prevent food-dumping or deprivation which only add stress to stress.

Strategy 2: Keep a "Survival Kit"

Headed into the wilderness, you take a survival kit. Headed into the wilderness of a daily schedule, you also need a nutrition survival kit. Well-intentioned as we may be, when stress or hunger hit, our best eating plans can go out the window.

You'll want to keep handy:

Fruit. The carbohydrates and other nutrients in fruit provide fast energy and are easy to assimilate. Apples and pears travel well.

Low-fat protein. Low-fat cheese also travels well. At home or in the office, adding fruit to nonfat or low-fat cottage cheese or to natural yogurt turns it into a nutritionally balanced snack. A glass of soy milk also does the trick.

Fluids. We need fluids like water and natural juices to keep flowing throughout the day. They flush toxins from the body and keep us from suffering the stress and fatigue caused by even mild dehydration. Please note that drinking ice cold fluids can mildly shock the body. Taking in fluids at close to room temperature is a better idea.

Snacks. There are great, nutritionally balanced "snack bars" on the market today. Some, like Zone, Balance, and MetRx bars, have been created by doctors and nutritionists. And while other snack bars offer few health benefits (no matter what the wrappers say) or else taste like paste, these three brands are delicious!

If you're prone to stress eating, you need an alternate plan. Without one, you're more likely to stay stuck in the old, unhealthy patterns.

Foods and Stress

Sometimes we need to be aware that it's not how we eat but *what* we eat that stresses our system. Technically, just about any food can trigger a physical stress response. By that I mean most of us encounter particular foods or food groups that are harder for us to digest than others. One man's delicious broccoli dish is another man's digestive nightmare. At the most common level, the overeating we do as a culture is guaranteed to tax the body. Pushing back from the table just after our hunger is diminished and before the fuel tank registers "full" is a great habit of mindful eating.

Beyond this most basic problem we need to be aware of conditions and foods that cause stress.

Food allergies. Many of us need to be alert to the possibility of food allergies. Today, allergies to wheat and dairy products are fairly common and can wreak havoc on both the digestive and immune systems. It's possible to be allergic to almost any food type and to the additives used in our foods. Contrary to what many people believe, allergies don't always originate in childhood. They can emerge at any point in life.

If allergies run in your family, or if you suspect you suffer from food allergies, see your doctor, allergist, or a nutritionist. A simple elimination diet can sometimes target a problem that's gone on too long.

Ken suffered with digestive problems all his adult life. He rarely felt good. Often he felt sick, or at least uncomfortable and lethargic. Extra work or activity did him in. By accident, he noticed that when he eliminated bread and pasta from his diet for a few days, he felt great. His digestive problems ceased. Also, he had more physical energy, and mentally he was sharper than he had been in a long time. He also noticed he was no longer subject to mood swings. A visit with a qualified allergist proved he had been reacting to the gluten used in many products, including breads and pastas. Modifying his diet relieved Ken's system of extra stress, and he started to feel great and enjoy life.

Acid stomach, irritable bowels. There are a number of digestive problems related to what we eat. All are signs that our system is being overtaxed. Two of the most common disorders are acid stomach (and reflux) and irritable bowels.

Acid stomach can be caused by eating foods that are highly acidic or which produce excess stomach acid—for instance, tomatoes, red meats, or oily/greasy foods. It can also be caused by an intolerance to any food our system finds hard to digest.

Not only does acid stomach interfere with digestion and assimilation of nutrients, it's often accompanied by acid reflux. Reflux is a painful condition, and is sometimes itself a sign that the body is under stress. The terrible burning and chest pressure that result from reflux are caused when the valve closing off the esophagus from the stomach relaxes, allowing stomach acids to flow back up and burn the esophageal lining. Reflux is a condition requiring medical attention, not merely over-the-counter antacids.

Likewise, irritable bowels is a general term referring to a condition in which the intestines—the large intestines in particular—are stressed and unable to perform their normal digestive function.

Irritable bowels can be caused by foods to which we're allergic or which we cannot digest. The result can be discomfort, bloating, loose stools, and even minor bleeding…and stress to our whole system. A physician's care is required to stave off more potentially serious problems.

Caffeine. We, the people, in order to form a more manageable day, love our caffeinated drinks in the morning. Some of us go on loving them to the tune of four, five, or ten cups a day. (We also love our chocolate which contains caffeine, not to mention future rolls of fat.) Caffeine does give us the jolt we're looking for, but it also raises our stressor-response impulses. So even slight irritations can be magnified.

Jolting our heart with caffeine is *not* the way to get energy. Underneath the protests—"But I love coffee!" or "I need my afternoon cola"—usually lies the real need, which is for an A.M. or P.M. rocket booster. Caffeine's "quick-pick-me-up" effect is not really worth the stress overload it produces on our cardio-vascular and central nervous systems, not to mention that it overtaxes the adrenal gland's production of epinephrine and norepinephrine, which are already depleted when we're under stress. Nor is using caffeine as a so-called energizer worth the mild form of substance-dependency it encourages. And the truth is, a dependency reveals that in some way we're most likely living out of balance. (Wouldn't more sleep or more recreation be a healthier response than more coffee or cola?)

Sugar. Sugar consumption is at an all-time high in Western countries. The average person eats the equivalent of 20 teaspoons a day. That's up roughly 25 percent since 1984, despite the advent of the popular artificial sweetener Aspartame.

Sugar intake causes blood-insulin levels to peak and drop like the Dow Jones average. This is *not* an exaggeration. If you experience that famous sugar rush, followed by a crash and need for a nap, you know it's true. Such peaks and dips stress our body, which fights first to deal with the "energy" overload, then struggles to regain when the energy blast is over.

Keep in mind that the refined sugar contained in, say, chocolate, ice cream, corn syrup sweetener, candy, or beverages is not the only source of the famous sugar rush. Foods like bread and pasta break down quickly in the mouth and hit our system with a load of sugar all at once.

"GET RIPPED"

∼

One of the key ingredients in many so-called natural "energy boosters" and "fat burners" is guarana. Guarana is a substance derived from a South American plant. It even shows up in these new natural "muscle-building formulas" that promise to help you "get ripped." And these formulas are expensive.

Here's the kick in the head: Guarana is just a more highly concentrated dose of—guess what? *Caffeine!* No wonder you feel more energetic. No wonder you can pump more iron.

Many of these formulas also contain ephedra and/or the herbs mahong or yohimbe—all of which are now posted on the FDA's cautionary list.

Do the people who sell these "formulas" tell you what to do when your metabolism is boosted and you'll eat anything that can't run away?

And as for the wide use of guarana, doesn't selling caffeine under another name more expensively, while making "wonder promises," give new meaning to the term "getting ripped"?

Salt. Salt plays a major role in affecting blood pressure, even in the average person. Too much sodium is also responsible for fluid retention when those fluids should be available to flush toxins from our body.

We just do not need as much sodium in our diets as we get. Not by far. There is plenty of sodium in many foods in their natural state. Ever read the label on skim milk? One eight-ounce glass contains 130 mgs. of sodium. Surprised? Nonfat yogurt holds 150 mgs. per cupful. Tuna offers 250 mgs. in two ounces (hardly enough for a sandwich!). Your average wheat bread packs 150 mgs. in each slice.

HOW DO YOU RATE
(IN THE BLOOD PRESSURE DEPARTMENT)?

∾

High blood pressure is divided into several ratings:

Borderline = 120-160/ 90-94
Mild = 140-160/ 95-104
Moderate = 140-180/ 105-114
Severe = 160+/ 115+

Doctors are mostly concerned when the diastolic pressure (the second number) is up, but systolic pressure matters, too. Let's say you have a normal diastolic pressure of 82, but a systolic reading up in the low-mild range, around 145. (Your reading would be "145 over 82.") You have twice the chance of suffering a life-threatening heart episode as someone with a normal reading.

This warning aside, it's important for all adults to know and keep track of their blood pressure. Many pharmacies now have do-it-yourself machines you can use anytime.

Make a note of your blood pressure on a small card and keep it in your wallet or purse. Check it at least once a quarter to detect any change.

Strategy 3: Sugar and Salt Switcheroo

Looking for literal sugar substitutes? Try stevia, which is an herb and a simple carbohydrate, or fructose.

Rice syrup, date sugar, and barley sugar, though complex carbohydrates, can also be used without the quick-rush/quick-crash effect.

If you have never tried salt substitutes, now is the time. Delicious herb blends give a tangy flavor to meat, soup, and eggs. Also try Chinese Five Spice as a great addition. You won't miss the salt.

Strategy 4: Practice "Smart Shopping"

Who would go to a grocery store thinking about shopping smart to beat stress? Not many people, right? *Exactly.* That's why the overall strategy in this chapter is based on mindfulness. At least take a moment to think about this, with grocery shopping in the back of your mind.

Almost every medical authority, including the Joint National Committee on Detection, Evaluation, and Treatment of High Blood Pressure, has agreed on the most effective overall treatment for stress and hypertension.[11] The conclusion is that nondrug therapies top all medical therapies. A wide range of stress interventions are recommended. But topping the list is *what you put in your grocery cart.*

And with just a few wise tips, you actually can shop to beat stress and its effects. (The first two are these: Pick a cart that doesn't have one wobbly wheel, and plan in advance to be polite to the people who leave their carts in the middle of the aisle while worrying over cat-food brands.)

Here is a simple strategy for shopping.

Smart shopping. The tendency is to shop the perimeter of the grocery store *last* because that's where the perishables are. Reverse that strategy.

Shop the whole perimeter of the store first. When you think about it, you'll realize almost all the natural and whole foods are here: fish, meats, fruits, vegetables, dairy products, and usually breads. If you ate nothing but what you bought from the perimeter, you would be eating a pretty good diet.

One goal of "smart shopping" is to keep you from spending a lot of time in the "jungle" aisles where all the sugar-, sodium-, and preservative-laden foods lie in wait.

Forget dawdling along to the Muzak. When you machete your way into that jungle of aisles, go in with a list to use as your map in…and out. Nutritionally, your most important purchases from these aisles will be whole grains, dried beans, (natural) cereals, oils, and spices.

By this point, your cart will be filling up with great nutrition (*that's the point*), and you'll start to be more mindful of additional items you put in your basket. You'll start to think, "Do we need these chips?" and "I've got fresh chicken—why not boil it and use the stock for soup instead of buying these canned soups that are full of sodium?"

Add to the list. Certain foods are known to benefit people under stress, because they're high in compounds that help reduce the effects of hypertension. Here are some top picks that are easy to work into a daily menu:

- Turkey, tuna—contain tryptophan (needed to produce the brain's neurotransmitters, which help regulate mood as well as sleep)
- Celery—high in 3-n-butyl phthalide
- Garlic and onions—rich in sulfur-containing compounds
- Green, leafy vegetables—great source of calcium and magnesium
- Whole grains and legumes—for fiber
- Citrus fruits, broccoli—any whole foods high in vitamin C

Strategy 5: Menu for That "Big Day"

Are you facing a big meeting? Just want to get through a day without riding the up-and-down, stressed-or-sleepy coaster? You may know to avoid candy to keep from experiencing the famous "sugar rush" and dip, but sugar is the Shirley MacLaine of food substances: It has "previous lives." Without knowing it, we can set ourselves up for a huge downer by eating the wrong foods early in the day, or when we definitely need to be "up" and alert.

Avoid eating starchy carbohydrates like breads, pasta, and certain grains in big doses. They quickly turn to sugar and trigger insulin production, which can swiftly bring on that "woolly headed" feeling.

Instead, keep your body's insulin production more level by making meals of these foods:

- *Modest portions of lean proteins*—like broiled or baked chicken, fish, or turkey, or very small portions of red meat
- *Large portions of fruits and vegetables*—avoid only the starchy ones

- **Very small amounts of fat**—like the kind found in olive or fish oils

If you're a juice drinker, check the container. Even frozen concentrates that look healthy can be loaded with corn sweeteners that will nuke your blood-sugar level. Instead, drink plenty of natural juices (which contain fructose) or fresh water (with a lemon or lime twist, if you prefer).

Under pressure, you'll keep a clear head, feel more alive, and be sharper if you eat mindfully.

Strategy 6: Stop Using Drugs, Alcohol, and Tobacco to Relieve Stress

Those who regularly use alcohol to "relax" and "unwind" or as a "nightcap" and sleep aid need to rethink this strategy. The dependency factor aside, alcohol remains in the bloodstream for many hours. Long after the need to relax or sleep is past, alcohol can still be at work. We may take a drink to help us sleep and wake up with no noticeable hangover. Yet the effects of alcohol can remain with us into the morning. In response, we reach for a caffeinated drink to turbocharge the engine, and begin the unhealthy cycle all over.

Face the fact. It's time for a change. There is no good reason to use alcohol as your sole stress-relief "strategy." Not one.

Likewise, if you have developed a dependency on drugs—either prescription or the illegal kind—to "calm you down," you need to try another course. Most psychotropic drugs lose their effectiveness, forcing you to switch from drug to drug or to take a higher dose to get the same effect.

If you need medication for a specifically diagnosed condition, continue under the care of your physician or psychiatrist. If not, you're far better off using natural means to relax and de-stress.

And finally, although using tobacco products seems to offer a mildly calming effect, the health risks far outweigh the extremely limited benefits. That calming effect is largely the result of the deep inhaling and slow exhaling that accompanies smoking. While the breathing pattern is actually very good for inducing calm, the toxins you're inhaling are killing you. If your excuse for smoking is "to calm my nerves" or even "just for pleasure" here's a thought: *Quit.* Decide that you will no longer be a dupe of the tobacco industry.

6

The Peaceful Apothecary

Some of the herbs and supplements discussed in this chapter are known to react with certain medications. Others will have an adverse effect on certain health conditions such as pregnancy, high blood pressure, depressive disorders, and others. And as yet it's not known which herbs react negatively when taken with other herbs.

Some, but not all, contraindications are mentioned.

Consult your health-care professional to create the health plan that is safe and right for you.

You may find current information on herbs and other supplements—including recommendations and cautions—on-line at www.consumerlab.com.

For years, vitamins and other dietary supplements were in the province of "health-food nuts" and superathletes. Herbs came from strange little people who lived alone in the woods and gathered roots.

Today, supplements are mainstream business. Even health-insurance companies are offering supplements for sale through on-line buying.

Still a bit of controversy remains, and it's fair to note it.

The Court of Public Opinion

Claims. Many people swear they've been cured by using substances with names like "Butcher's Broom," "Sheep Sorrel," and "Slippery Elm Bark." The claim is that supplements (sometimes in combination with diet, spiritual disciplines, and/or exercise) have cured people of conditions ranging from cancer to toenail fungus.

Objections. Quite a few medical doctors shrug off these reports and insist these "illnesses" were probably psychosomatic (a physiological response to a mental or emotional trigger). The "cure" these people experienced came from a "placebo effect." Taking *anything* would have helped them so long as they *thought* it would help.

Other doctors won't recommend the use of herbs based on scientific grounds. First, little is known about the active chemistry of many substances. Even if it works, we often don't know why it works—that is, what part of our physiology it is affecting. For instance, many people are using St. John's Wort to help with depression. But it's unclear which of the brain's neurotransmitter chemicals the herb's active chemistry affects. Nor do we know enough about its potential long-term side effects.

Second, because only the manufacturers regulate quality control right now, the value and consistency of the doses can vary widely in each lot. In fact, in some tests, capsules of a given substance have been found to contain none of the herb or its active ingredients listed on the label. So, suppose you're *really* counting on that dose of St. John's Wort to help you. You'll be greatly shortchanged if what you're swallowing in that particular capsule is mostly some kind of "stabilizer" or "filler."

The bottom line is that many doctors don't recommend herbs and supplements because they haven't been trained in the use of these substances. Only recently have medical schools added courses offering such training. Therefore, the medical profession is necessarily conservative and cautious.

Objections overruled. Those who use herbs and supplements dispute the objections with sensible answers of their own.

Isn't it just as possible that you can trigger a placebo response by using a pharmaceutical as a natural substance? And yes, we know what's in every prescription drug regulated by the government, and we know the potency is stable. But we also know that many of these man-made synthetic drugs can have harmful side effects. At the mild end, they can range from weight gain to drowsiness. Taken long term, some have proven to cause serious damage—for instance, to the heart, liver, and other major organs.

WATER, WATER, EVERYWHERE

～

It's always a good idea to drink plenty of water, and especially when you're taking supplements. Many people work their way up to six to eight 8-ounce glasses a day.

(By the way, no need to worry that you'll be answering the call of nature four zillion times a day. Your body adjusts.)

Drinking water throughout the day is beneficial in several ways. It helps your kidneys to function better by flushing your body of toxins. It prevents electrolyte imbalances, which affect mood. And it prevents dehydration, which can occur in both warm and cold weather, making you feel fatigued. It also offers some weight-loss benefit.

Purchasing your own filtration pitcher, like those sold by Brita, pays off very quickly if you've been buying bottled water.

Also work your way up the thermometer from "ice-cold" to room temperature. Very cold drinks give the body—especially an overheated one—a mild shock.

For a cool, refreshing drink, mix the juice of three or four lemons or limes in a tall pitcher of water. Mix in a natural sweetener like stevia or fructose to taste, and stir in 1/4 to 1/2 teaspoon cayenne. You won't taste the cayenne, but the active ingredient, capsaicin, will act as a mild stimulant, helping flush your system faster and giving you a natural pick-me-up.

Add ice and…bottoms up!

As a result, many people have decided they would just as soon take their chances and get help from a natural substance. Also, most people who take herbal supplements know that it takes time for the active ingredient to build to a therapeutic level in the bloodstream. And they also realize that (as with many medicines) it's important to continue taking the supplement over time to maintain effective levels. They know, in the case of the calming and mood-stabilizing supplements, one dose taken at the onset of stress won't do it.

Therefore, many people have simply made supplements a part of their daily regimen.

What follows is a list of the most commonly recommended vitamins, natural supplements, and herbs taken to relieve the symptoms of stress. Many of the nutrients suggested below are available, of course, in food. But taking them in capsule form, or in tea, is likely to give you a higher, more concentrated, and therefore more therapeutic dose.

A Small Apothecary
of Vitamins, Supplements, and Herbs

∽ ∽∽

The Vitamin Shelf

- *Vitamin B complex.* This family of vitamins is necessary for a host of important body functions. They help the nervous system function well, aid in producing energy, assist the adrenal gland in producing hormones, and help the brain generate the neurotransmitter chemical serotonin. Low levels of serotonin are associated with anxiety and depression. Vitamin B-5 (pantothenic acid) is the most important anti-stress vitamin. B vitamins are rapidly depleted from the body when we are under stress. B complex can be taken orally in doses of 100 mg. daily. B-5 can be taken in 100 mg. doses three times a day. Under severe stress conditions, a physician may opt to give intramuscular injections of B complex.

- *Vitamin C.* This vitamin is essential to adrenal gland function, which produces anti-stress hormones. Stress depletes us of Vitamin C. Therefore, it is also one of the most important vitamins in reducing stress. Vitamin C with bioflavanoids is highly recommended and can be taken in doses of 3,000 to 10,000 mgs. daily. Higher doses of Vitamin C should only be taken with adequate amounts of water—a minimum of 16 ounces taken at the time of the dosage. Without adequate water, kidney stones can sometimes result.

- *Vitamin E.* This vitamin is needed to boost immune function, which is compromised by stress. Vitamin E can be taken in doses of 400 IUs.

The Mineral Shelf

- *Calcium, magnesium, potassium.* These three minerals should be taken in combination for effective use by the body. In therapeutic doses, they release tension from the muscles and also have a calming effect on the emotions. Potassium is another essential in adrenal gland functioning. Often calcium and magnesium are sold in combination, and sometimes all three are combined as well.

  Calcium can be taken in doses of 2000 mgs. daily. In order to help calcium combine with magnesium and potassium, it should be taken in its chelate form. Only take calcium in its lactate form if you are not allergic to lactose. Magnesium can be taken in 1000 mg. doses every day. Potassium can be taken in doses of 100 mgs. per day.

- *Zinc.* Is essential to boosting immune function. Zinc can be taken in 50 mg. daily doses.

The Amino Acid Shelf

- *L-Lysine.* This amino acid is effective in treating cold sores often triggered by stress. L-Lysine can be taken in 1000 mg. doses each day.

- *L-Phenylalanine.* This amino acid comes in two forms: the L form (recommended here) and the DL form (not recommended). L-Phenylalanine is used in the treatment of depression, which often accompanies stress. It produces neurotransmitter chemicals in the brain and norepinephrine, a hormone produced by the adrenal gland that can have a slight mood-boosting effect. *L-Phenylalanine is not recommended if you are pregnant or suffering from panic or anxiety attacks, high blood pressure, PKU (phenylketonuria), or if you have had cancerous melanoma.* L-Phenylalanine can be taken in 1000 mg. daily doses.

- **L-Tryptophan.** This amino acid helps, among other things, to alleviate stress. It is a link between vitamin B-6 and the production of neurotransmitter chemical serotonin. However, after potential links between certain blood disorders were established, the U.S. Food and Drug Administration recalled all products containing L-Tryptophan from the market. It's now available only through illegal foreign sources and is thus not recommended. L-5-Hydroxy Tryptophan is a full-spectrum herbal formula containing a range of vitamins, herbs, and amino acids that produce the same relaxed mental state as L-Tryptophan. Recommended doses for this and other L-Tryptophan substitutes vary by manufacturer.

  Manufacturer warnings indicate that these substances are not for use if you are pregnant or taking an MAO inhibitor. Taking these products in large doses can also impair ability to drive and use heavy equipment.

- **L-Tyrosine.** This amino acid is often used in the treatment of stress-related problems such as anxiety and depression. It can stimulate the production of norepinephrine and has a mood-elevating effect. L-Tyrosine can be taken in 1000 mg. doses daily.

For maximum effectiveness, doctors and manufacturers recommend that amino acids be taken on an empty stomach, in 500 mg. doses, first thing in the morning and before bed at night. They should also be taken along with Vitamin B-6 and Vitamin C for better assimilation by the body.

The Hormone Shelf

- **Melatonin.** This hormone is manufactured in the body from serotonin and secreted by the pineal gland found at the base of the brain. Though melatonin's function is still being studied, it is known to play an important role in regulating the body's internal "clock," controlling periods of sleep and wakefulness. Normally, melatonin is released by the pineal gland as evening darkness falls, and is suppressed by daylight. During stress, the natural melatonin-production cycle is greatly disturbed—sometimes severely affecting the ability to fall asleep and to experience deep, REM sleep, which is essential to well-being. Melatonin can be taken in doses of 3 mgs. 20 minutes before your desired bedtime.

Though melatonin is widely used you should consult with your physician if you are pregnant or if you have an autoimmune condition or depressive disorder.

ESSENCES AND HOMEOPATHY

～

Flower essences are sold in many health-food stores today. They claim to contain the "essence" or vibrational energy of various wildflowers and tree blossoms in a base of alcohol. They are administered by a dropper, on or under the tongue.

The makers of flower essences don't claim to cure illnesses per se. Rather, they address inner conflicts (such as fear, uncertainty, loneliness, and despondency, among others) that prevent us from being our true selves. No scientific evidence whatsoever exists to prove or disprove the effectiveness of these products.

Homeopathic "medicines" are also sold in many health-food stores and even some pharmacies. Homeopathy is based on "the Law of Similars." According to this "law," taking a tiny microdose of a substance that might cause a certain illness if taken in a larger dose, can actually make you well. (Lest you dismiss this idea, the same principle is used in treating allergy patients with microdoses of the offending allergen.)

In homeopathy, Coffea Cruda is recommended for insomnia from stress, and *Antimonium crudum* may be used for indigestion and headaches, along with other "medicines."

In the United States, controversy about the effectiveness of homeopathy remains strong. If you choose this form of treatment, it is best to seek the help of a homeopathic doctor, instead of relying on self-treatment with substances purchased over the counter.

The Herb Shelf

As mentioned at the outset of this chapter, proceed with care when taking herbal supplements. Herb-to-herb reactions are not uncommon, and certain herbs may also react with your metabolism. Check with a knowledgeable pharmacist for known herb-to-herb and herb-to-drug reactions.

Directions and dosages will vary according to concentration and the manufacturer's recommendation.

- *Barberry (also known as Oregon grape)*, is used in the treatment of stomach upset associated with stress and nervous tension and as a sedative. Effects are felt in one to two hours. Barberry is available in capsules.

  Pregnant women should not take barberry, as it may stimulate uterine contractions. Given its sedative effects, using barberry in conjunction with Ativan, Valium, or Xanax is not recommended.

- *Catnip* is a member of the mint family and has a mildly relaxing effect. It is also known to relieve nausea and gas. Catnip is taken as a tea or in extract form.

- *Chamomile.* No single ingredient has been identified to account for the various health benefits of this wonderful herb, which has been known to ease stomachache and colitis, as well as to soothe, relax, and help induce sleep. Chamomile comes loose for tea, in capsules, and in extract. Sometimes people with weed allergies—particularly ragweed—will experience reactions to chamomile.

- *Cramp bark* is also known by a more pleasant name: *Black Haw.* Lydia Pinkham's Vegetable Compound, one of the most popular women's medicines of the nineteenth and early twentieth centuries, contained this herb whose legendary effects as a muscle relaxant come to us through Native American medicinal lore. Its overall antistress effects are powerful, as it is a general relaxant for muscle "jumps" and spasms. If you're a man, go ahead and call it Black Haw if that will help you feel better about using it. Cramp Bark/Black Haw is taken as an extract.

- **Fennel** is a member of the celery family, known to help relieve the stomach upset and bowel tension that accompanies stress. Several health-beneficial essential oils and other compounds have been identified in this herb, accounting for its medicinal effectiveness. Fennel comes in several forms: tea, capsule, and extract.

  While there is no evidence yet that fennel in the above forms interacts with any pharmaceutical drugs, be warned that fennel oil, taken internally, has been known to cause serious side effects.

- **Feverfew** comes from the aster family and has escaped from the garden into the wilds where it's identified by its daisy-like flowers. In antiquity, it was known to cure headaches and "melancholy." In modern times, the main active ingredient in this herb, parthenolide, has been found effective in treating headaches and, if used regularly in therapeutic doses, in preventing migraines. Extracts are also used as histamine blockers in the treatment of allergies. Effects when dealing with serious migraines can take up to a month. If you are prone to chronic stress headaches, however, it's worth it to give this herb's active ingredients time to build up in your system. Feverfew is taken in capsule and in raw leaf form.

  This herb should not be used by pregnant women as it is known to bring on menses. It may also affect blood clotting, so its use before or after a surgery is not recommended. Those allergic to ragweed should use feverfew cautiously or not at all.

- **Kava** has been used for centuries in Polynesian cultures and has gained a good reputation in the American health-care community because its anxiety-reducing properties can be as effective as benzodiazepine drugs like Ativan, Valium, and Xanax. It relieves stress-induced muscle cramps and is a strong mood-elevator. Kava is taken as a tea or in juice, in capsules, and in extract.

Kava in higher doses can have side effects such as drowsiness and impaired reaction time. Its effectiveness can equal that of prescription drugs. Therefore, *you should not take kava if you're planning to drive.*

Kava should not be taken by individuals with Parkinson's disease. It should not be taken if you use alcohol or prescription sedatives. Kava is likely to increase the effectiveness of other sleep- and relaxation-inducing supplements, and for that reason should be used cautiously in combination.

In one known case, kava seems to have heightened the effect of a benzodiazepine drug, inducing a non-fatal coma. Though it is a rare instance, ask your physician for guidance and supervision if you are taking one of the drugs mentioned above for the treatment of anxiety, stress, or panic attacks before adding this herb to your relief strategy.

- *Lemon Balm* (also known as bee balm or sweet balm) shows up in many "salt substitute" flavorings and is known for— what else? — its pleasant, lemony aroma. Folklore tells us it has been used to ward off colds and flus for centuries and to relieve "nervous agitation" and as a sleep aid. (A topical application is used to cure cold sores.) Greatest effects are felt in a week. Lemon balm is taken in tea, capsule, and extract forms.

- *Linden Flower.* In Europe, the use of this aromatic herb is second only to chamomile, and the two are often combined. Linden flower is used to fight flus and colds, but by far its greatest benefits lie in its ability to help relieve hypertension with its calming effects. It also acts as a mood lifter. Effects are noticeable within an hour, increasing over a few days. Linden flower comes as a tea or an extract.

- *Meadowsweet.* If this herb is unknown to you, ever heard of aspirin? In the early 1800s, the anti-inflammatory chemicals known as salicylates were first extracted from meadowsweet after its long history as a medicine that helped relieve fevers, headaches, and rheumatic pains. This one is good for stress headaches, especially if you cannot tolerate aspirin and other over-the-counter medicines. Effects are felt in an hour. Meadow-sweet gives you a choice: tea, capsules, or extract.

- **Passionflower.** When Spanish explorers came across this trumpetlike, bright-red flower in the New World, its three styles reminded them of the three nails that held Christ to the cross—hence the name. It has been used widely in Europe in the treatment of stress-induced agitation, nervous exhaustion, and insomnia. Effects may be felt within minutes for some, in a week for others. Passionflower can be taken as a tea, in capsules, and in extract form.

  This herb is not recommended for pregnant women unless its use is approved by a health-care professional. Because it can cause drowsiness, you should avoid driving or operating equipment. Allergic reactions and asthma are reported in rare instances. Though no interactions have been reported at this time, you should seek medical advice before using passionflower in combination with drugs or other herbs.

- **Siberian Ginseng.** As early as 100 B.C. the Chinese were using this potent herb as an overall tonic. When purchasing, make sure you are buying *eleuthero*, as it is also known, or that its scientific name, *E. senticosus*, appears on the label, as substitutes and impostors abound. This herb is known to boost resistance to the mental and physical effects of stress, and to positively affect blood pressure elevation. Effects begin immediately and are most noticeable in a week and thereafter. Siberian Ginseng is used in many teas in combination with other herbs, but for stress relief it is best when taken in capsules and extract.

  Pregnant women should note that there is little information on the use of this potent herbal medicine during pregnancy and should therefore avoid it.

- **Skullcap** is known to relieve sleep disturbances, nervous hypertension, stress headaches, and mood swings. (In seventeenth century Europe it was known as "mad dog herb" from its effectiveness in treating rabies.) It's an effective sedative when stress and anxiety won't let you sleep. Effects are felt within a few minutes. Skullcap comes in a tincture or extract.

- **St. John's Wort** is widely used today to relieve anxiety, balance emotions, treat mood swings, and alleviate mild to moderate depression. It's thought by researchers that the active compounds in this herb—hypericin, pseudohypericin, and hyperforin—may assist in neurotransmissions within the brain, thus producing antianxiety and antidepressant effects. Effects are noticeable in one to two weeks. St. John's Wort is taken as a tea, in capsules, and in extract.

  You should not rely on St. John's Wort as your main course of treatment if you are experiencing panic attacks or if you are seriously or clinically depressed. Seek the help of a physician or psychiatrist. It should not be taken if you are using MAO inhibitors. It doesn't react well with certain protease inhibitors (check with your physician). Also, taking this herb is known to cause skin hypersensitivity and to increase the danger and damage of sunburn. St. John's Wort may affect the metabolism of Coumadin, Clozaril, Elavil, Haldol, Theo-Dur, Tofranil, Zyflo, and Zyprexa.

- **Valerian** has become a popular sleep aid that quiets the mind and helps release tension in the body. Use of valerian goes back to the ancient Greeks, and by the eighteenth century, Europeans were using it to cure nervous disorders and panic attacks. Effects are felt in 30 minutes to an hour. If you take a large dose late in the day, you may experience sound sleep, but you are likely to wake up feeling groggy the next day. Build up to the dose that helps you, without causing this side effect. Valerian is taken in capsule and extract forms.

  Valerian is known to interact with barbiturate drugs, and it should not be taken if these drugs are being used. If you're using benzodiazepine drugs like Ativan, Valium, and Xanax, you should not take valerian. This herb is also not recommended for pregnant women. Since it may also cause frequent urination, it may not be the best herbal sleep aid for those already suffering from disorders that cause this problem. Valerian is known to affect the metabolism of Coumadin, Clozaril, Elavil, Haldol, Theo-Dur, Tofranil, Zyflo, and Zyprexa.

- ***Willowbark*** also contains salicylates, the active ingredient in aspirin. As a result, it is an effective remedy for stress headaches. While it may be more effective for some people than its herbal counterpart meadowsweet, willowbark contains tannins which may cause upset stomach. Effects are felt in one to two hours. Willowbark can be taken as a tea, in capsules, and in extract.

"O, the powerful grace that lies in herbs!"
—SHAKESPEARE

℞

"HOUSE RULES" FOR TAKING HERBS

～

Remember…some herbs contain milder doses of active ingredients than synthetic drugs. Some are very potent and should not be used in combination with pharmaceuticals or with other herbs. Herbs also, generally, take longer to reach their effective level in the bloodstream.

Therefore, keep in mind some rules when using herbs to combat stress:

1. ***Consult your health-care professional if you have questions or doubts.***

2. ***Read labels carefully.*** Abide by manufacturer directions and warnings. Build up to full doses.

3. ***The effectiveness of herbs (vitamins and other supplements, too) is easily destroyed by using certain strong substances at the same time***—for instance, caffeine, nicotine, and alcohol.

4. ***The active compounds found in herbs need time to build up in the bloodstream to be effective.*** Even so, while taking herbs (and other supplements) be sure to keep your system flushed by drinking plenty of water.

5. ***Take time to do your own research.*** Not every doctor or pharmacist will be knowledgeable about herbs, their uses, and possible interactions. Seek professional opinions and help, but remember that you are the one most responsible for your own well-being.

6. ***If you experience adverse reactions after taking an herbal remedy, stop taking it at once*** and seek a physician's opinion and help. In an emergency, call your local poison control center for help.

7. ***When you are ready to discontinue the use of an herb you have used over a period of time,*** come off it gradually as you would a medication. You don't want to cause new stress to your system by quitting suddenly. Ease off over the period of at least a week.

7

Releasing Physical Stress

*D*o any of these verbal "snapshots" seem familiar?

- About mid-morning, you feel a slight tension in your neck just behind your ears at the base of the skull. In an hour you feel pain in your temples. You can't get comfortable. By the end of the day you're headachy and stiff.

- Mentally and emotionally, you "play shortstop" all day. You handle whatever life, work, and your family happens to line drive in your direction—not to mention all your own responsibilities, too. By bedtime, the mild asthma you haven't experienced for more than a year is making it hard to breathe.

- You put in a *very* hard day of physical labor. Or at least you used to. Now, if the truth be known, you're a collection of aches. You have pain in your major joints much of the time.

- After a stressful fight with someone you love, you go to bed exhausted, but you don't sleep well. You awake in the morning, wondering how you're going to drag your weary bones out of bed to deal with the day. Later, as you lift a simple bucket of paint, your back twinges and goes out.

- Your spouse, your kids, your boss—someone important in your life levels you with a harsh criticism. Five minutes ago you were feeling up. After this "punch in the soul," you feel drained of all energy and just want to sleep. A day later, you come down with a whale of a sinus infection.

Much has been documented about the mind-body connection and the effects of stress on physical health. These "snapshots" are common examples of the way stress can throw us off balance and compromise our physical well-being.

Earlier, we saw how it's possible to be a "stress battery," storing negative core beliefs, emotions, and the energy of unresolved conflict. In this chapter we want to look at the way stress is stored in the body and, more importantly, how to release it.

First, let's take a closer look at some common ways stress builds up in our physical being.

Storing Physical Stress

Erin

Erin sits at a computer terminal all day, with a one-hour break during which she gulps down her lunch. Even with an "ergonomic" chair and keyboard, her shoulder and neck muscles remain rigidly in the same position for hours.

For Erin, the problems begin by mid-morning when the muscles at the top of her shoulder start to fatigue. As lactic acid builds in these muscles, they tighten. As they stress, they pinch the nerves that radiate out to the small muscles running up the sides and back of her neck. These muscles also fatigue, and the problem spreads to the muscles that radiate up around her ears to her jaw and facial muscles…and to the nerves and muscles spreading across her temples to her forehead. In addition, the same muscle-stress reaction is radiating down through the long muscles that support Erin's spine, and even into her lower back.

What's going on here?

Muscle fatigue and stress are what makes Erin's back and neck muscles clench, resulting in the sometimes dull, sometimes splitting headaches she experiences. By the end of the afternoon, even though she's "just been sitting at a desk all day," she feels depleted.

℞

DOES YOUR JOB GIVE YOU A PAIN IN THE NECK?

∽

The average human head weighs in at 8.8 pounds. Is it any wonder we get neck aches and headaches from sitting in one position at a desk, or a computer, or behind a steering wheel all day? (For comparison, try holding a ten- or even a five-pound weight out from your body at arm's length and see how long it takes for your shoulder muscles to give out!)

If your job requires you to sit with your head in the same position for a long time, it's likely to give you, literally, a pain in the neck. You can do something about neck stress. Try these simple stress-relieving exercises (and to help you remember, you may want to do them, say, every two hours on the hour):

- Gently tip your head to the left and count to ten. Then tip to the right and count to ten. Allow the muscles to relax and stretch naturally. Don't force them. Use forefingers and thumbs to knead muscle knots.

- Now gently tilt your head forward, chin to chest. Then slowly tilt your head gently back, chin to heaven.

- Remember: Perform these movements gently and slowly. Never roll your head, as this may damage the delicate disks in your neck.

- As you do the exercise, concentrate on your breathing. Slowly, through the nose, fill your lungs. Exhale through your mouth.

Try this, and see how it helps prevent neck fatigue and muscle-tension headaches...*and* helps you feel more alert, too.

Your job doesn't have to give you a pain in the neck. Not literally, anyway!

Will

Will has always loved to keep moving. You couldn't pay him enough to sit behind a desk. Construction seemed like the best job choice, since it keeps him outdoors most of the time, and the physical activity helps him keep the physique he acquired playing sports. Even now, with 40 coming at him, he looks better than many guys in their twenties.

But in the past three years he's hardly spent a single month without some physical ache or problem. First, it was his right elbow. Then a muscle-pull in his left forearm took four months to heal. Last year, both shoulders started to ache whenever it rained. Now, if he does any lifting, one of his knees hurts with the intensity of a bad toothache.

Will tells himself he just needs to "work through" the pain. But in fact, the repetitive and high-impact nature of his work has compromised his musculoskeletal system. His muscles, cartilage, joints, and bones are overstressed almost every day. This stress is "stored" in the sense that it's slowly wrecking his physical body.

Laura

Laura is a manager's manager. She keeps upper management happy, chairs meetings, sets schedules, meets deadlines, resolves employee problems, rides the budget, and greets clients. Only Laura's family and secretary know about the many physiological problems that plague her.

It's not that the physical demands on her are high-impact like Will's. Or repetitive and muscle-cramping like Erin's. But the pressures that weigh on Laura inwardly translate into constant stress on her cardiovascular and musculoskeletal systems. She is experiencing a co-lateral discharge of energy, meaning simply that mental tension is being subtly passed on to her body in constant physiological tension.

In fact, Laura's body is taking constant abuse and storing far more stress than she knows. If she were to stop and concentrate on her physical being at any given moment, she would notice these characteristics: There is always muscle tension somewhere in her body. Her breathing is usually shallow, not relaxed and deep. She may be more susceptible to colds and minor infections than other people. On vacation and on days off she still feels like a coiled spring, making it hard to relax.

People in Laura's position are often at higher risk of suffering heart attacks, and diseases related to a suppressed immune response. Women who experience this chronic co-lateral discharge of nervous energy may also experience menstrual and related problems.

Julie

Julie opted to stay at home and raise the three kids while Matt worked. They're good kids, really, but they're small and the demands are great. While the two older ones are scrapping, the baby is crying for a diaper change. Her whole day is consumed by the demands of motherhood. By supper time, Julie describes herself as "wired and witchy."

Throughout the evening, as the kids get more tired and cranky, Julie's stress builds. When they're in bed, she feels fatigued, but also scattered and distracted. She winds up staying up till midnight—long after Matt's asleep—puttering in the kitchen, eating, or reading.

While Julie doesn't feel all that energetic, the fact is, she has more physical energy to burn. But since it's been unfocused all day, it's become nervous stress-energy. Rather than working it out, she has worked it *in*. As a result, her sleeping-waking cycle is being edged out of sync. As a side effect, her intimacy with Matt is diminished.

This May Sound Crazy, But...

When stress attacks our bodies, we can help ourselves by discovering the wonderful benefits of physical stress-release techniques.

In an earlier chapter, we considered the possibility that the opposite of work is not rest, but enjoyment. That's because, as we saw, what we do to earn a living is more connected to our sense of purpose and meaning, rather than to the expense of physical energy. So connecting and balancing those two aspects of our life—purpose and enjoyment—works toward restoring a sense of peace and well-being. In this chapter we want to look at the connection between our actual expense of physical energy and its opposite: rest and the restoration of our body.

This may sound crazy, but most of us will find tremendous benefit from expending a good bit more physical energy than we do.

"No," you're thinking, "this doesn't sound crazy. It *is* crazy." You're thinking of the whole list of responsibilities you carry and how hard it is to cover all the bases as it is. You can feel it coming: a pitch about getting started on an exercise regimen.

Not so. There are several techniques for releasing physical stress, and yes, one of them is exercise. But the point is to find what works for you, not to induce more tension by adding to your inner stresses the guilty feeling that you "should" be exercising.

Far better to start with the truth that most of us are not *inactive*. We're usually very busy and occupied most of the time. We spend our days in homes or offices doing work that involves talking and attending meetings around tables (a.k.a. "talking in circles"). We're occupied with many small, repetitive tasks that require mental focus, people skills, word skills, and probably some technical abilities, such as computer skills.

Or we may work at a job that requires us to be on our feet all day, stocking, lifting, constructing. Maybe driving and delivery. This work requires us to put out more physical energy than someone in a sedentary job, for sure.

An old proverb says, "The sleep of a hardworking man is sweet." But for many of us, sleep is not restorative as it is meant to be.

In both cases, the problem is this: We're involved in physical activity that only depletes us, and so it's stress-inducing. That's because we're involved in activities that are all *take*.

When we're involved in things that take, take, take from us all day, we don't work out our stresses. We store them in soul and body. A proverb from several millennia ago states that, "The sleep of a hardworking man is sweet."[12] (Don't shoot. We include women, too.) Obviously, the guy who came up with that envisioned someone who has pleasantly worked until he is "tuckered out," feeling deeply at peace as his head smacks the pillow. He has literally "worked out" whatever stress life tried to work in.

The proof for many of us that we haven't worked the stress out of our physical being is the fact that our sleep is light and unsatisfying, not deep and restorative as it is meant to be.

What does it take to "work out" our physical stress?

Do Try This at Home

Warning: You're about to read a pitch for something that will greatly benefit you in the long haul. If you're just looking for immediate help, skip to the next section. (But I hope you won't.)

In order to work out physical stress, we need two things: Cardiovascular good sense and musculoskeletal good sense.

Cardiovascular Good Sense

Normal, at-rest breathing is fairly shallow to begin with. We use only a third to a half of our lungs' capacity. Waste gases take a longer time to clear the lungs. And this is under good conditions.

Stop! Take a moment right now and breathe in slowly through your nose until your lungs fill to capacity. Then exhale quickly through your mouth. In childbirth classes, this is called a "cleansing breath" for very good reason. You just expelled a lot of carbon dioxide, and injected more oxygen into your blood. See how good and relaxing this feels? Your blood, organs, and cells thank you.

When we feel stressed and tense, our breathing becomes more shallow. (When we're startled, of course, we hold our breath and momentarily stop breathing altogether.) It's a natural reflex.

The effect of shallow stress-breathing is that waste gases literally "back up" in our lungs, blood, tissues, muscles, and cells. Instead of being expelled, toxins build up in our system. Our body can't function in a healthy manner, and we experience the negative results of "stored stress," that tired, achiness in the actual fibers of our being.

It makes simple good sense to add a regimen of cardiovascular workouts to our stress-relief strategy. The best workout strategy, of course, is one that's a regular part of your life routine.

Musculoskeletal Good Sense

Breathing is not the only mechanism we have for cleansing our tissues and relieving stress. When they're in use our muscles act as simple and effective "pumps" to move waste out. The good news is, we don't have to be bodybuilders. We just need to have muscles that are in use.

In use is the key term here. This means more than the normal workout our muscles get in a given day as we walk, stand, climb steps, and lift light loads like briefcases, purses, and grocery bags. It means more than the use they get during light work such as sweeping, raking, or digging little holes in the garden. It can even mean more than swinging a hammer at a construction job all day.

For our musculoskeletal system to "work out" the tensing effects of stress, two things are required.

First, a muscle needs to carry a weight load through its full range of motion. Range-of-motion exercises—which include both weight-bearing and stretching exercises—benefit the muscles, ligaments, and tendons. Without range-of-motion exercise, these important parts of our body weaken and shorten, which sets us up for strains and more serious injuries.

What does a range-of-motion exercise look like?

Right now extend one of your arms out in front of you, palm up. Make a fist. Slowly raise the fist, bending your elbow and tightening your arm muscles as you do so, until your knuckles almost touch your shoulder. Hold it and keep reading.

The second thing needed is alternating periods of muscle contraction and relaxation.

Now slowly extend your arm to the original position, relaxing it. Release the fist. You've completed a simple range-of-motion exercise for the bicep, tricep and forearm muscles.

We did this to illustrate two important points.

It's important to recognize that we can be active all day and use very little of our muscle capacity. Our muscles aren't being used to pump out the toxins that naturally build up in them. Our tendons and ligaments aren't stretched in ways that give them a healthy elasticity.

It's just as important to recognize that we can be involved in hard work all day (or use certain muscle groups a lot, such as when we're on our feet all day) and still not use our muscles in a way that benefits us. That's because many types of hard work, even most construction jobs, don't allow us to use our muscles' full range of motion or allow for periods of contracting and relaxing.

This explains why Will, whom we met earlier in this chapter, can engage in hard physical labor every day and not get a well-planned, stress-releasing workout. He can even boast more and bigger muscles than other guys, and actually be less healthy in terms of both cardiovascular and musculoskeletal well-being.

The main point is this: Even after a tiring day, it makes good sense to use a regimen of physical stress-release strategies. Whereas we've seen that certain kinds of activities wear us out and leave us storing stress, others can help us to both counter the stress-inducing events of the day and build us up physically for the long haul.

Even if we don't develop a regular workout regimen as part of a long-term strategy, we can still experience the immediate calming benefits of physical stress-releasing techniques. The recommended strategies are divided into two groups for a good reason we'll discuss later.

THE TAKE-ACTION STRATEGIES

Okay, so you come home at the end of a day and you feel fatigued. That easy chair sure looks inviting. But as the saying goes, "Don't go there, Honey." Difficult as it is to believe, you'll feel less tired and better all around if you work the physical and emotional dregs of the day out of your body by taking action.

Instead of turning on the news or grabbing the paper (aren't you trying to *avoid* more stress?), slip into sweats or some other comfortable clothing that allows you to move freely. What kind of action you take and how much of it is entirely up to you.

Attention, please. Obviously, you'll need to take into account health conditions and possibly consult a physician before starting a prolonged or more intense regimen. You also want to ease in and build over time, rather than starting out at an intense level. In this way you'll avoid both injuring yourself and the tendency to give up because you've overtaxed yourself too quickly.

I recommend simply trying one or more of the following techniques until they help you to take your mind off the day's hassles, and until you feel good, calm, and ready to really relax.

Strategy 1: Stretching

Stretching is not only an excellent way to end the day, but to start it as well. A modified stretching workout can also be done at work, on a plane or train, or in a car (but in case it needs to be said, *not* if you're the driver).

The nice thing about stretching is that you don't need to buy anything. You just have to own a body. Stretching is probably one of the most underrated and underused of the physical stress-release techniques, and yet it yields great benefits. If you don't believe it, the next time you're stiff and sore, try this—an exercise I call "Using Your Head—and Some Other Parts, Too."

1. *Sit in an open space on the floor with your legs comfortably apart.* Remember that all movements should be slow and gentle. Don't force a tight muscle. Work out its tension slowly. The goal is to express lactic acid and other natural wastes that have built up. Repeat each step until the muscle group you're working relaxes. Use cleansing breaths before and after each stretch described.

2. *Use your head.* That is, use it to perform the gentle head and neck stretches described earlier.

3. *Use your shoulders.* Raise your left shoulder slowly toward your left ear. At the same time, push your shoulder forward, until you can feel the back muscles between your shoulder blade and spine stretch. Relax. Repeat, using the right shoulder.

4. *Use your arms.* Extend your arms in front of you and lay one hand on the other, palms down. Slowly raise your arms straight over your head, allowing your diaphragm to expand as you inhale. Reach toward the sky and gently stretch your abdominal muscles. Exhale.

Still stretching, use your right hand to slowly draw your left arm across and in front of your face. Feel the muscles down the back side of your left ribs stretch. Repeat for the benefit of your right side.

Now, using your right hand, gently draw your left arm across and *behind* your head. Feel the muscles in your shoulder and down the side of your left ribs stretch. Repeat with your right arm. (You *are* remembering to breathe, aren't you?)

5. *Use your legs.* With arms outstretched, hands one over the other, slowly bend at the waist and reach for your left foot. Keep your left leg straight—don't bend the knee, and don't force. Feel the buttock and hamstring muscles stretch. Repeat to make the right side happy.

6. *Use your feet.* Back in the sitting position, arms relaxed at your sides, point your left foot, and tense the muscles up the front of your leg. Hold for a moment, then relax. Repeat on the right.

You've just completed a full-body stretch, stimulating your metabolism and blood flow *and* releasing some stress your poor muscles were storing.

If you would rather have an eye put out than use more vigorous stress-relief strategies, stretching and acupressure are your definite "keepers."

Strategy 2: Acupressure

Like stretching, this is another technique that's simple and has tremendous stress-releasing benefits, and yet it's little-used. Acupressure is the technique of massaging or kneading muscle trigger points to help a stressed muscle group relax.

Acupressure practitioners claim that this technique releases both physical and emotional stress. It's more likely that emotional stress is handled by dealing with spiritual core issues and relationship conflicts. Nonetheless, the physical stress-release benefits of acupressure are truly great. Acupressure does not claim to cure, but can help to relieve the discomfort of a wide variety of physical stresses and ailments. These include everything from allergies, ankle and foot problems, anxiety and nervousness, arthritis (both osteo and rheumatoid), backache and sciatica, chronic fatigue, colds and flu (including deep chest coughing and difficult breathing), depression, earaches, headaches and migraines, to sinus problems, stomachaches (indigestion and heartburn), and toothaches.

Two of the most common stress-related problems, of course, are headache and neck ache. The following diagrams will help you locate the pressure points most effective for releasing stress stored as muscle tension.

Releasing a Headache or Neckache

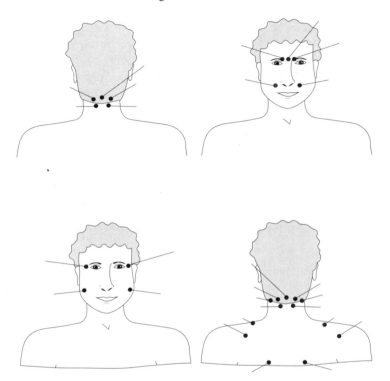

For a complete guide to acupressure stress relief, refer to *Acupressure's Potent Points: A Guide to Self-Care for Common Ailments* by Michael Reed Gach (Bantam, 1990).

Strategy 3: Light Aerobics

Included in this strategy are danceercise, walking, short-course jogging, roller blading, and easy cycling.

It's hard to convince those who haven't tried it, but a short aerobic workout even after a long day at work is incredibly rejuvenating.

It raises the heart and metabolism rates and takes the muscles through a good range-of-motion workout.

A word of encouragement can help this technique work for you: You'll feel the benefits of light aerobics immediately in terms of the great night's sleep you'll feel after burning off stored stress-energy. If you try this two to three times a week, in only one to two weeks you'll also experience a wonderful return of youthful, vital energy. (Sure beats relying on caffeine to get you going!)

A wonderful guide for creating a light aerobic strategy that works for you is *Walking Medicine: The Lifetime Guide to Preventive & Therapeutic Exercise-Walking Programs* by Gary Yanker and Kathy Burton (McGraw-Hill, 1990).

MUSIC...AND THE RIGHT SHOES

∼

Music has long been known to have a powerful effect on the physical body, for ill or for good. By joining forces with various natural body rhythms, pounding drums and sounding trumpets have stimulated men to battle, and softly sung melodies have soothed babies to sleep since time began.

Listening to music that matches the motion and rhythm you want to achieve is one secret behind better, more effective aerobic workouts. Music that's slow and fluid works wonders during a stretching workout, and livelier dance music can give you an added charge of energy while jogging or cycling. (Just remember to stay alert for traffic.)

Shoes. Keep in mind that when you're running or jumping, your feet are absorbing as much as two to three times your body weight! So three words apply: *Don't buy cheap.* No, you don't need $150 athletic shoes, but you do need enough cushion and support to help your feet have a nice time while you're getting slim, trim, and rejuvenated.

Strategy 4: Intense Aerobics

Sometimes after a tense day, nothing helps like "going for the burn." Intense aerobics may be the ticket for you. A more intense aerobic workout would include activities like long-course jogging, running, hiking, or mountain biking.

In order for an aerobic workout to be beneficial, it's important for your heart rate to remain elevated for at least 30 minutes, but not *too* high. You want your heartbeat to remain within the target heart-rate range that's appropriate for your age. When the heart beats above its maximum range, you enter an anaerobic state and muscle tissue begins to break down.

The following chart will help you "keep the beat" in the correct range.

Target Heart Rate Range	
Age	Range
25	117 to 156 beats per minute (20 to 26 beats per 10 seconds)
35	111 to 148 beats per minute (19 to 25 beats per 10 seconds)
45	105 to 140 beats per minute (18 to 23 beats per 10 seconds)
55	99 to 132 beats per minute (17 to 22 beats per 10 seconds)
65	93 to 124 beats per minute (16 to 21 beats per 10 seconds)

Measuring Your Heart Rate: Place the tips of your index and middle fingers lightly on your opposite wrist below the base of the thumb. If it's resting on a bluish line, that's your radial artery and you're right on target. Count the beats for 10 seconds and multiply by 6. Increase or decrease your workout intensity to keep your heart within the target range. When your workout ends, it's important to let your heart rate drop below 100 before allowing yourself to stop moving.

For a great workout reference, check out *Workouts for Dummies: A Reference for the Rest of Us* by Tammilee Webb with Lori Seeger (IDG Books Worldwide, 1998).

LIMITS

∿

Everything has limits, including exercise. Most of us, however, are not in danger of exceeding the limits when it comes
to exercise. But for those who are, keep the following rule in
mind: Five aerobic workouts a week, of 45 minutes duration
each, is the *maximum* amount of aerobic activity that's beneficial for you. Beyond that limit, your body is overstressed
and immune abilities decline.

Yes, Virginia, there can be too much of a good thing.

Strategy 5: Weight-Resistance Workouts

For some of us, nothing but shoving heavy weight around will
do to release the stress that's pent up in our muscles. We have to
honor the need we feel to push against the thing that's resisting
us...and to sense the opposing force move away. Pushing weights
satisfies something in us. Either that, or for some odd reason we just
enjoy a bit of grunting and straining. Weight resistance workouts
can include calisthenics or weight training, and can range from light
to heavy lifting.

If you are trying weight-resistance training (lifting) for the first
time, or if you are getting back into it for the first time since high
school or college, read this:

Gentlemen, let's take off the gloves here. You may *remember* how
much you could bench press back then, but "back then" was 10, 20,
or 30 years ago. Plus, if you consider the more sedentary lifestyle
you've probably lived together with the inflated estimation most of
us males have of our strength, you've got a potentially serious injury
in the making.

Ladies, you may desperately want to shed those leftover baby-
having pounds and to release kid- and work-induced stress through

weight-resistance training. But no one says you have to fit into a dress the size of a mailing tube or look like Xena, warrior princess.

A good rule of thumb: *Easy does it.* If you plan to use weight-resistance workouts in your stress-release strategy, an excellent resource is *The Gold's Gym Weight Training Book* by Ken Sprague (Putnam, 1993).

THE TAKE-A-BREAK STRATEGIES

Strategy 6: Massage

As one massage therapist puts it, massage is "100 percent good for you, with no artificial additives or ingredients, and it's easy to do." For a full-body massage or just a back rub, you'll obviously have to enlist the help of a friend or massage therapist. If you're working with a friend at home, get yourselves a great manual like the one listed below. If you're ready to sign up with a pro, look for a Licensed Massage Therapist (LMT).

For amazing massage moves that you can do yourself to release physical stress, try these:

Headache and sinus congestion relief. Using your thumbs, hook the upper inner corners of your eye sockets, where the nose and brow bones meet. (Not as terrible as it sounds.) Press up.

Headache relief point #2. (Don't dismiss this headache cure until you've tried it!) Using the thumb and index finger of your right hand, squeeze the webbing between the thumb of the left hand. Slide your thumb from the big knuckle of the left index finger out toward the wrist. Repeat this move, using the left hand to massage the right.

Facial tension relief. The jaw and cheek muscles carry an incredible amount of stress. Using your thumbs, press in at the center of your jaw muscles about an inch in front of your ears. Move thumbs in a circular motion. Then move your thumbs up about an inch to the underside of your cheek bones. Press, and slide your thumbs in a small arc around the base of this bone. (This is a favorite!)

Upper back relief. Several massage moves help here.

First, with your right hand, reach across your body and wrap your hand around under your left armpit, with the fingers resting on the outside of your left shoulder blade. Using the index and middle finger, knead the muscles. (It's almost guaranteed you don't know how tense these muscles are until you try this!) Now be nice to the right side.

Second, with your right hand, reach across your body and behind your left shoulder, with the fingers resting on top of your left shoulder blade. Use all four fingers, knead from the outside of the shoulder blade toward your neck. Little surprise pockets of tension await you here, too.

A wonderful massage resource (minus photos of models who make you feel bad about how you look) is *Massage for Dummies: A Reference for the Rest of Us* by Steve Capellini, LMT, and Michel Van Welden, PT, NT (IDG Books Worldwide, Inc., 1999).

Strategy 7: Chiropractic

So you've tried the massage techniques, and the muscles along your neck are tight as a bowstring. Or you turn your upper body to one side, and your lower back says, "Not today, kid." Maybe you've even seen a massage therapist who said, "Darned if I can get these muscles to relax."

Chiropractic therapy is the next step, and an important strategy for many people in releasing stored muscle stress. Expect to be treated with hot packs, vibrational massage, and mild *electro-stimulation* even before you see the doctor. The therapist is loosening those stubborn muscle knots in preparation for the real treat.

A licensed chiropractor has had college training in the art of musculoskeletal manipulation. This means he or she knows how to carefully manipulate joints that have been pulled out of alignment by stressed and overtense muscles, which is why you're in discomfort. The release of locked-up joints and muscles can have a deep tranquilizing effect. Plan a nap or rest after your visit.

To find a qualified chiropractor near you, contact the American Chiropractic Association at 1-800-986-4636.

Strategy 8: Sleep

This must be a joke, right? Do we have to be *told* it's time to get our jammies on and get into bed?

Apparently so. Or sleep deprivation wouldn't be one of the most widespread contributors to depression, anxiety, sickness, and stress among adults. Many adults average only five or six hours of sleep a night. As the resulting physical stress builds, we probably average only about one hour of the rejuvenating REM sleep our body desperately needs before an alarm jars us rudely awake.

AH, THE BOUQUET!

∼

Aromas have been shown to have a wonderfully relaxing effect. Some of the most popular and effective of the aromatic essential oils that are known to aid in stress relief are:

- *For tension and anxiety:* chamomile, clary sage, geranium, lavender, rose, sandalwood, and wintergreen.
- *For an energizing uplift:* cardamom, coriander, grapefruit, peppermint, and rosemary.

Aromatherapy oils are very concentrated, and a few words of instruction will help to make the experience enjoyable.

1. Keep oils away from your eyes and away from small children. Never ingest them.

2. For an aromatic and stress-releasing massage, dilute 10 to 12 drops in one ounce of a natural carrier oil, such as baby or mineral oil, or even an unscented body lotion.

3. For a relaxing bath, mix 2 to 10 drops of essential oil in a tub of warm (not hot) water.

4. Freshen a room with relaxing scent by adding 4 to 6 drops of your favorite essential oil to one cup of water in a plant mister…and spray.

The kind of heavenly tranquility we've all sought since the Garden of Eden can be ours—or at least a hint of it—through the magic of essential oils. Guaranteed: You don't want to miss it.

Now hear this! Sleep is a required event in your daily schedule! Sleep is also required in decent quantities.

For those of us who think we can race into bed like we're sliding into home plate and knock off a night's rest in five hours (why waste time?), here are a few tips to help us get the necessary sleep every fiber of our being craves.

Sleep after a prep time. Most of us require some prep time during which to calm down. Getting drowsy in front of the TV is not what I mean. Better prep for sleep includes gentle stretching and sacred or inspirational reading to put both body and soul at ease.

Sleep a long time. Whatever time you aim to be in bed, most of the time your head hits the pillow an hour later. Set your bedtime early to correspond with your body's internal clock. Remember, as daylight fades, your body's production of melatonin, the sleep-inducing hormone, increases. Fighting your body's natural rhythm by pushing yourself to stay up late isn't the wisest thing to do.

Sleep with a backup plan. It's 3:06 A.M. and you're staring at the ceiling. The last thing you should do is fret about not getting enough sleep and how miserable you'll be the next day. The temptation is to get up and read, or even to work. (What are you thinking?) A far better backup plan is to stay in bed and use relaxation techniques, including deep breathing, slow stretching, meditation, and "connected" prayer. Even if you fail to fall back to sleep, your body will gain more benefit from these calming strategies than from you punching the pillow.

The bottom-line question is: Will we honor our body's natural rhythm?

Plan for a decent and full night's sleep regularly, and you'll be amazed at your ability to handle the stress that comes with the daylight hours.

"One from Column A, One from Column B..."

The truth is, expending enough physical energy and getting enough rest are opposite ends of a wonderful balance. In the hustle and hassle of life, few of us strike the right balance without planning.

This brings us back to the important reason the above strategies were divided into two groups. The reason is simply that we need to plan both into our day in order to work stored stress out of our body.

Imagine that our waking/sleeping cycle is a seesaw. We need take-action strategies to burn off nervous tension that's jangling around in our muscles and neurons, so we can drop into deep sleep at night. And nightly we need to plumb the depths of the unconscious bliss we call sleep in order to launch ourselves up and out into each bright new day.

The question is, Will we honor our body's natural rhythm?

Why not take a few moments to skim the strategies again, then consider making a simple behavior contract with yourself? Choose one or more of the take-action strategies and one of the take-a-break strategies to rebalance your life...and take a giant step toward overall well-being.

Encore!

There is one final, simple secret that will help us move from stress to peace. It is this: *Find the way to take delight in living.* In so doing, we move many miles down the road toward personal and lasting peace.

To delight in living is the simplest and yet the most challenging step of all. No one can do it for us. We must do it for ourselves. But when we find the right path, we can offer each other some clues. Here then are a few directional markers.

- *Find the way to delight in the events of your life—all of them, even the tough ones. Trust that it will all make sense in the end.*

- *Find the way to delight in the things you own—all of them, even the plainest and most common. Realize that what you own is not you.*

- *Find the way to delight in the people in your life—all of them, even the hard-to-take ones. Learn how each one deepens you in some way.*

- *Find the way to delight in knowing that your life is good and that it's a gift—all of it, the part you're living now and the greater part you'll live when this part's over.*

- *Find the way to live for a purpose that will outlast you.*

- *Find the way to know and delight in the One who created you.*

And in closing, here's a wise suggestion from a beautiful, cheerful, and contented little girl named Sarah Beth, who lives in the midst of an imperfect, stressful world every day.

Notes

2. I Corinthians 6:19

3. Thomas Moore, *Original Self* (New York: Harper-Collins Publishers, 2000), pp. v-vi.

4. Psalm 139:13; Proverbs 20:27.

5. Abraham Joshua Heschel, *God in Search of Man,* (New York: Noonday/Farrar, Straus and Giroux, 1955), p. 6.

6. Proverbs 23:7.

7. Matthew 5:45.

8. Revelation 21:5.

9. Romans 8:31.

10. In Psalm 139: 13, the writer represents the simple, ancient wisdom that our soul is the seat of our passions and drives. In our "inmost being" resides the fire that causes us to do the things we love to do. These human drives were seen as a divine gift, the spark given to each of us to guide us on the natural course that's right for our life.

11. Michael Murray, N.D., and Joseph Pizzorno, N.D., *Encyclopedia of Natural Medicine,* 2nd Edition (Rocklin, CA: Prima Communications, Inc., 1988), p. 525.

12. Ecclesiastes 5:12.

The New Nature Institute

The New Nature Institute was founded in 1999 for the purpose of exploring the connection between personal health and wellness and spirituality, with the Hebrew-Christian tradition as its spiritual foundation.

Drawing upon this tradition, the Institute supports the belief that humankind is created in the image of God. We are each body, mind, and spirit, and so intricately connected that each aspect of our being affects the other. If one aspect suffers, our whole being suffers; if all aspects are being supported we will enjoy a greater sense of well-being.

For this reason, the Institute engages in ongoing research in order to provide up-to-date information that supports a "whole person" approach to wellness. Most especially, research is focused on the natural approaches to wellness that support health and vitality in the body, the mind, and the spirit.

Healthy Body, Healthy Soul is a series of books intended to complement treatment plans provided by healthcare professionals. They are not meant to be used in place of professional consultations and/or treatment plans.

Along with creating written materials, *The New Nature Institute* also presents seminars, workshops, and retreats on a range of topics relating to spirituality and wellness. These can be tailored for corporate, spiritual community, or general community settings.

For information contact:

The New Nature Institute
P.O. Box 568
Round Hill, Virginia 20142
Attn. David Hazard

(540)338-7032
Exangelos@ aol.com